Photograph of Richard Wagner, signed and inscribed
to Mrs. Gustav Schirmer, wife of the
founder of the house.

THE MASTERSINGERS
OF NUREMBERG

An Opera in Three Acts

Music by
RICHARD WAGNER

Complete Vocal Score in a
Facilitated Arrangement by
KARL KLINDWORTH

English Translation by
FREDERICK JAMESON

G. SCHIRMER, Inc., NEW YORK

CHARACTERS

HANS SACHS, Shoemaker	. . . . .	*Bass*
VEIT POGNER, Goldsmith	. . . . .	*Bass*
KUNZ VOGELGESANG, Furrier	. . . . .	*Tenor*
KONRAD NACHTIGALL, Tinsmith	. . . . .	*Bass*
SIXTUS BECKMESSER, Town Clerk	. . . . .	*Bass*
FRITZ KOTHNER, Baker	. .	*Bass*
BALTHASAR ZORN, Pewterer	. .	*Tenor*
ULRICH EISSLINGER, Grocer	. . . . .	*Tenor*
AUGUSTIN MOSER, Tailor	. . . . .	*Tenor*
HERMANN ORTEL, Soap-maker	. . . . .	*Bass*
HANS SCHWARZ, Stocking-weaver	. . . . . .	*Bass*
HANS FOLTZ, Coppersmith	. . . . .	*Bass*

Mastersingers

WALTHER VON STOLZING, a Young Knight from Franconia *Tenor*

DAVID, Sachs's 'Prentice . . . . *Tenor*

EVA, Pogner's Daughter . . . . *Soprano*

MAGDALENA, Eva's Attendant . . . . *Soprano*

A NIGHT-WATCHMAN . . . . *Bass*

Men and Women of all Guilds, Journeymen, 'Prentices, Girls, Folk

SCENES OF THE ACTION

FIRST ACT: *The Interior of St. Katharine's Church*

SECOND ACT: *In the streets, before the houses of Pogner and Sachs*

THIRD ACT: (Scs. I-IV) *Sachs's workshop*, (Sc. V) *An open meadow on the Pegnitz*

PLACE: *Nuremberg*

TIME: *About the middle of the sixteenth century*

LIST OF SCENES

In the English version of the text, all names of persons (even those of Walther, David, and Eva), and all exclamations, except where they are obviously English, should be pronounced as in German.

Die Meistersinger von Nürnberg

von
RICHARD WAGNER.

Vorspiel.

Klavierauszug
von Karl Klindworth.

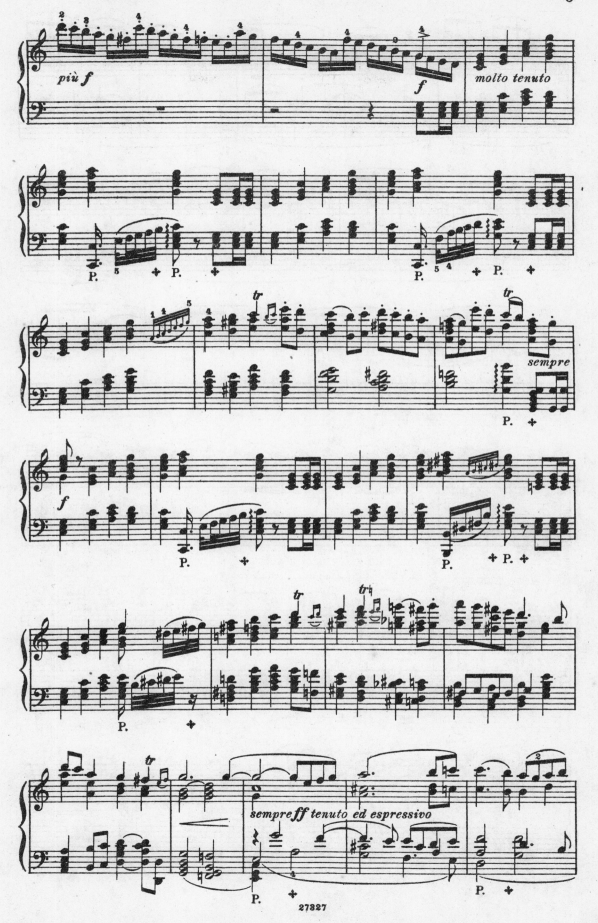

Bewegt, doch immer noch etwas breit.

molto espress.

Mässig im Hauptzeitmass.
dolcissimo ed espress.

allmählich immer stärker

stacc.

Erster Aufzug.
Erste Scene.

Die Bühne stellt das Innere der Katharinenkirche in schrägem Durchschnitt dar; von dem Hauptschiff, welches links ab, dem Hintergrunde zu, sich ausdehnend anzunehmen ist, sind nur noch die letzten Reihen der Kirchenstühlbänke sichtbar: den Vordergrund nimmt der freie Raum vor dem Chor ein; dieser wird später durch einen schwarzen Vorhang gegen das Schiff zu gänzlich geschlossen.

In der letzten Reihe der Kirchenstühle sitzen Eva und Magdalena; Walther von Stolzing steht, in einiger Entfernung, zur Seite an eine Säule gelehnt, die Blicke auf Eva heftend, die sich mit stummen Gebärdenspiel wiederholt zu ihm umkehrt.

First Act.
First scene.

The stage represents an oblique view of the church of St. Katharine; the last few rows of seats of the nave, which is on the left stretching towards the back, are visible: in front is the open space of the choir which is later shut off from the nave by a black curtain.
In the last row of seats Eva and Magdalena sit; Walther von Stolzing stands at some distance at the side leaning against a column with his eyes fixed on Eva, who frequently turns round towards him with mute gestures.

wil - lig dei - ne Tau - fe nahm,
by thy hand bap-tized to be,

wil - lig dei - ne Tau - fe nahm,
by thy hand bap - tized to be,

wil - lig dei - ne Tau - fe nahm,
by thy hand bap - tized to be,

wil - lig dei - ne Tau - fe nahm,
by thy hand bap - tized to be, (Eva's Blick und Gebärde sucht zu
(Eva by look & gestures attempts to

Belebend.

dim.

weih - te sich dem Op - fer -
chose the Cross for man's re -

weih - te sich dem Op - fer -
chose the Cross for man's re -

weih - te sich dem Op - fer -
chose the Cross for man's re -

antworten; doch beschämt schlägt sie das Auge wie- weih - te sich dem Op - fer -
der nieder.)
answer him, but casts her eyes down again ashamed.) chose the Cross for man's re -

nachlassend

piu p

pp

p cresc.

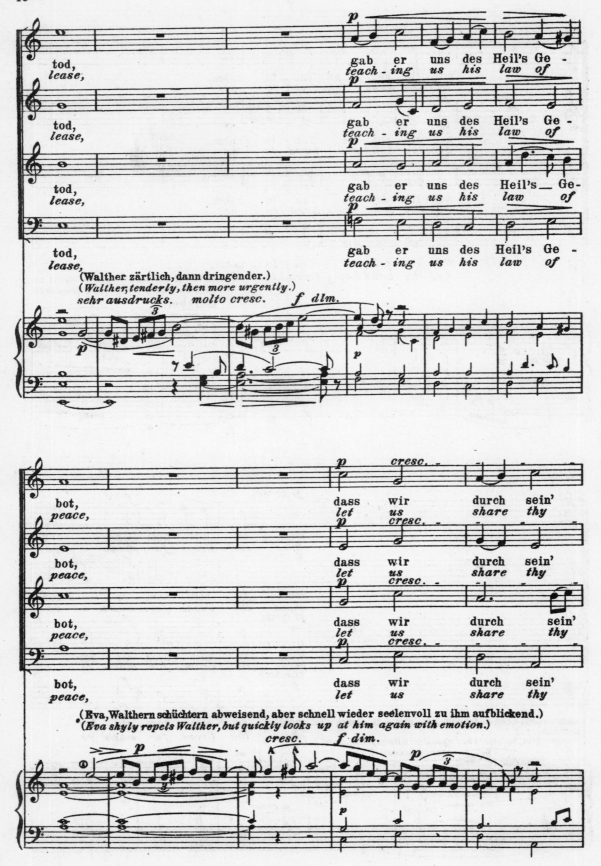

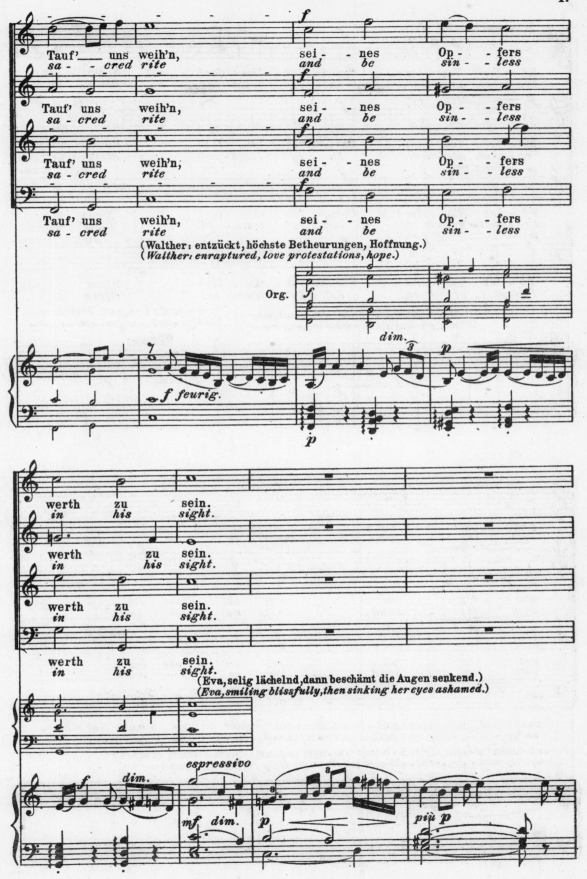

Tauf' uns weih'n, sei - nes Op - fers
sa - cred rite *and be sin - less*

Tauf' uns weih'n, sei - nes Op - fers
sa - cred rite *and be sin - less*

Tauf' uns weih'n; sei - nes Op - fers
sa - cred rite *and be sin - less*

Tauf' uns weih'n, sei - nes Op - fers
sa - cred rite *and be sin - less*

(Walther: entzückt, höchste Betheurungen, Hoffnung.)
(*Walther: enraptured, love protestations, hope.*)

Org.

f feurig.

werth zu sein.
in his sight.

werth zu sein.
in his sight.

werth zu sein.
in his sight.

werth zu sein.
in his sight.

(Eva, selig lächelnd, dann beschämt die Augen senkend.)
(*Eva, smiling blissfully, then sinking her eyes ashamed.*)

espressivo

18

27327

(Die Gemeinde erhebt sich. Alles wendet sich dem Aus -
gange zu, und verlässtunter dem Nachspiele allmählich
die Kirche. Walther heftet in höchster Spannung seinen
Blick auf Eva, welche ihren Sitz ebenfalls verlässt,
und von Magdalena gefolgt, langsam in seine Nähe
kommt.)

*(The congregation rises. All turn to the door and
gradually leave the church during the voluntary.)
Walther fixes his gaze in great anxiety on Eva,
who leaves her place at the same time and, followed
by Magdalena, comes slowly towards him.)*

(Da Walther Eva sich nähern sieht, drängt er sich gewaltsam durch die Kirchgänger zu ihr.)
(*Walther, seeing Eva coming, presses forcibly through the crowd to her.*)

EVA (sich schnell zu Magdalene umwendend.)
(*turning round quickly to Magdalena.*)

Mein Brauttuch, schau!
My kerchief, look!

WALTHER.

Verweilt!   Ein Wort!   ein einzig Wort!
Oh·stay!   *A word!*   *one single word!*

Lebhafter.

EVA.

Wohl liegt's im Ort _   MAGDALENA (Sie geht nach den Kirchstühlen zurück.)
*'Tis left be·hind_*   (*She goes back to the seats.*)

Vergesslich Kind!   Nun heisst es: such'!
Forget·ful child!   *Now I must seek!*

WALT.

Fräulein, ver-zeiht der Sit - te Bruch. Ei-nes zu wissen,
Maiden, for-give my bold ap-proach. Tell me but one thing,

Ei-nes zu fra-gen, was müsst'ich nicht zu bre-chen wa-gen? Ob Le-ben o - der
tell me, I pray you. To learn the truth what would I dare not? If life be mine or

Tod? Ob Se-gen o-der Fluch? Mit ei - nem Wor-te sei mir's ver-traut:— mein Fräulein,
death, if blest I be or banned? One sin-gle word will my fate de - cide:— fair maiden,

EVA.

MAGD. (wieder zurückkommend.) Oh weh! die Spange. (Sie geht abermals zurück nach hinten.)
(returning again.) *A-las! the buckle.* (She goes again to the back.)

Hier ist das Tuch. Fiel sie wohl ab? Ob
Thy kerchief's here. Lost is that, too? If

sagt....
say...

27327

WALT.

Licht und Lust, o-der Nacht und Tod? Ob ich er-fahr', wo-nach ich ver-
light and life, or night and death_ whether I learn the tid-ings I

lan-ge, ob ich ver-neh--me, wo-vor mir graut:_ mein Fräu-lein,
hope for, whether I hear what sore-ly I dread:_ fair maid-en

MAGD. (Wieder zurückkommend.)
(Returning again.)

Da ist auch die Spange._ Komm, Kind! Nun hast du Spang' und Tuch...
There hast thou the buckle._ Come child! Now hast thou clasp and scarf.

sagt....
say...

(Sie geht nochmals eilig nach hinten.)
(She goes again hastily to the back.)

O weh! da ver-gass ich selbst mein Buch!
A-lack! now I have for-got my book!

WALT.

Dies ei - ne Wort, ihr sagt mir's nicht? Die Syl- be die mein Urtheil spricht? Ja oder
The word I crave, you speak it not __ the word that will fore-cast my lot! Yes or

(entschlossen und hastig.)
(resolutely & quickly.)

nein!__ ein flücht'ger Laut: mein Fräulein, sagt, seid ihr schon Braut?
no __ a fleet-ing sound: are you as bride by promise bound?

MAGD. (die wieder zurückgekehrt ist, und sich vor Walthern verneigt.)
(who has again returned, curtseying to Walther.)

Sie da! Herr Rit - ter, wie sind wir hoch - ge - ehrt:
Sir knight, I thank you. great hon-our, faith, is ours:

mit Ev'chens Schutze habt ihr euch gar be-schwert. Darf den Be-such des
for E - va's es-cort receive our hearty thanks. May I make known your

24

27327

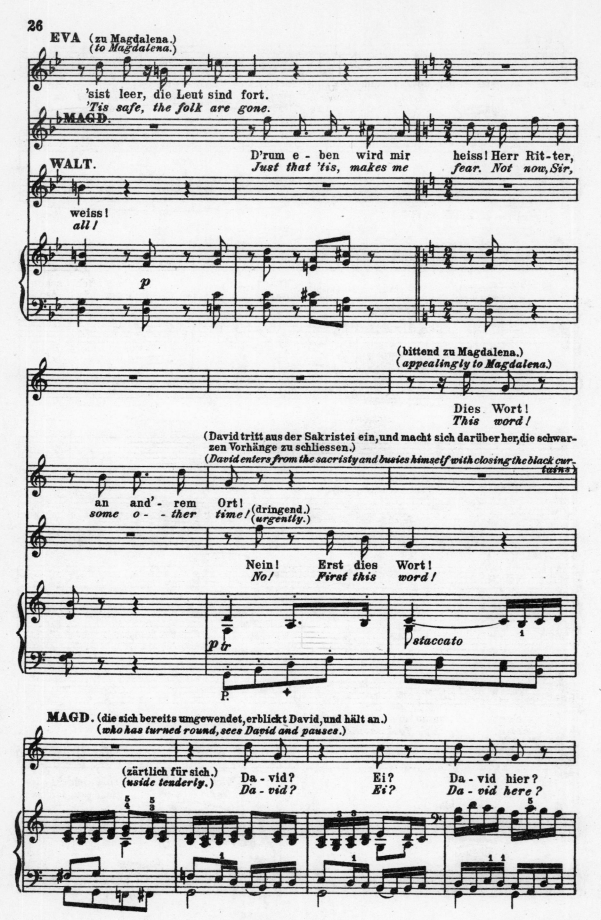

EVA (zu Magdalena.)
(to Magdalena.)

'sist leer, die Leut sind fort.
'Tis safe, the folk are gone.

MAGD.

D'rum e-ben wird mir heiss! Herr Rit-ter,
Just that 'tis, makes me fear. Not now, Sir,

WALT.

weiss!
all!

(bittend zu Magdalena.)
(*appealingly to Magdalena.*)

Dies Wort!
This word!

(David tritt aus der Sakristei ein, und macht sich darüber her, die schwarzen Vorhänge zu schliessen.)
(*David enters from the sacristy and busies himself with closing the black curtains*)

an and'-rem Ort! (dringend.)
some o--ther time! (*urgently.*)

Nein! Erst dies Wort!
No! First this word!

staccato

MAGD. (die sich bereits umgewendet, erblickt David, und hält an.)
(*who has turned round, sees David and pauses.*)

(zärtlich für sich.)
(*aside tenderly.*)

Da-vid? Ei? Da-vid hier?
Da-vid? Ei? Da-vid here?

27327

EVA. (zu Magdalena)
(to Magdalena)

Was sag' ich?   Sag' du's mir!
How tell him?   Speak thou then!

MAGD. (sie wendet sich wieder zurück, und zu Walther.)
(*she turns back again & towards Walther.*)

sempre p

MAGD. (zerstreut, oft nach David sich umsehend.)
(*at a loss, frequently looking round towards David.*)

Herr Rit - ter, was ihr die Jung-fer fragt, das ist so
The ans - wer you now would have, Sir knight, no sin - gle

leicht-lich nicht ge-sagt.   Für - wahr ist Ev'- chen
word can give a - right.   *For though be - trothed is*

stacc.

EVA (lebhaft unterbrechend.)
(*quickly interrupting.*)

Doch hat noch kei-ner den Bräut'-gam er-schaut!
Still hath no man yet the bridegroom be-held!

Pog - ner   Braut _   Den Bräut'-gam
E - va   held _   *None knows, in*

mf   *f*

EVA.
lass mich den Ritter ge-winnen!
help but my lov-er to win me!
Das e-ben
E-ven at
MAGD.
Sah'st ihn doch gestern zum er-sten Mal?
Yes-ter-day first didst thou hear his name?
dim.
p
f
p
P.
schuf mir so schnel-le Qual, dass ich schon längst ihn im Bil-de
once was my heart in flame; long had I looked on his im-age
f
p
f
dim.
sah! Sag',— trat er nicht ganz wie Da-vid nah? (höchst verwundert.)
fair! Say,— doth he not stand like Da-vid there? (in great astonishment.)
Bist du toll! Wie
Art thou mad? Like
p
f
mf
sf

EVA.

Wie Da-vid im Bild!
Like Da-vid the King!

MAGD.

Da-vid?   Ach!   meinst   du den Kö-nig mit der
Da-vid?   *Him*   mean'st   thou, with harp and crown and

Nein!   der,   dess'
No!   *he*   *who*

Har-fen und   langem Bart in der Mei-ster Schild?
scep-tre and   *flow-ing beard on the Masters' shield?*

Kie - sel den Go-li - ath war-fen,   das   Schwert im Gurt, die
bold - ly Go-li - ath vanquished: with   sword   at side and

EVA.

Schleuder zur Hand, das Haupt von lich-ten Locken umstrahlt, wie ihn uns Meister
sling in hand his head be-dight with locks of gold, as drawn by Mas-ter

Dü - rer ge - malt!
Dü - rer of old!

MAGD. (laut seufzend.)
(sighing aloud.)

Ach, Da - vid! Da - vid!
Ah, Da - vid! Da - vid!

DAVID (der hinausgegangen und jetzt wieder zurückkommt, ein Lineal im Gürtel und ein grosses Stück
(who has gone out and now returns, with a rule in his bell and a large piece of white chalk swing-

Da
Here

cresc.

dim.

MAGD.

Ach, Da-vid! Was ihr für Un - glück schuft!
Ah, Da-vid! Ill luck e - nough thou mak'st!

weisser Kreide an einer Schnur schwenkend.)
-ing by a string.)

bin ich; wer ruft?
am I; who calls?

sempre stacc.

27327

MAGD.

Da wär der Rit - ter ja am rech - ten Ort._ Jetzt Evchen,
So then the Knight has found his time and place._ Now E - va,

DAV.

reut.
well.

komm! Wir müssen fort.
come! We must a - way.

Er - war - tet den
Nay, wait for him

WALTH. (schnell zu den Frauen sich wendend.)
(*turning quickly to the women.*)

Zu Meister Pog - ner lasst mich euch ge - lei - ten.
To Master Pogner's door now let me lead you.

hier, er ist bald da. Wollt ihr Evchens Hand er - streiten, rückt
here, he soon will come. If 'tis E - va's hand you sue for, then

(Zwei Lehrbuben kommen dazu, und tragen Bänke herbei.)
(*Two prentices enter, carrying benches.*)

Zeit und Ort das Glück euch nah._ Jetzt ei - lig von
take the time and place that serve._ poco accel. *Now, hence let us*

MAGD.

drei-ster,   wird hier der Jun - ker heut' Mei - - - - - -
fas-ter,   if here this Knight be made Mas - - - - - -

Belebt. (♩ schneller als zuvor.)
EVA.

Seh' ich euch wie-der?
When shall I see you?

MAGD. (Sie drängt Eva zum Fortgehen.)
(She urges Eva to go away.)

ster!
ter!

WALTH. (Sehr feurig.)
(With much fervour.)

Heut' A - bend ge - wiss! Was ich will
This ev'n - ing, be sure! Nought shall dis-

Belebt. (♩ schneller als zuvor.)

wa - gen, wie könnt' ich's sa - gen?   Neu ist mein Herz, neu mein
may me, no pow - er stay me!   *New is my heart; life is*

Zweite Scene.

Second Scene.

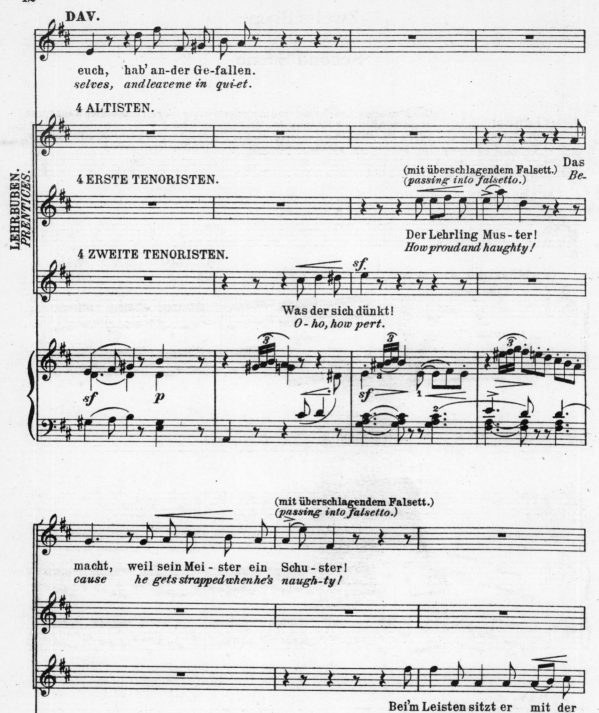

DAV.

euch, hab' an-der Ge-fallen.
selves, and leave me in qui-et.

4 ALTISTEN.

LEHRBUBEN.
PRENTICES.

4 ERSTE TENORISTEN.

(mit überschlagendem Falsett.)
(passing into falsetto.) Das Be-

Der Lehrling Mus-ter!
How proud and haughty!

4 ZWEITE TENORISTEN.

Was der sich dünkt!
O - ho, how pert.

(mit überschlagendem Falsett.)
(passing into falsetto.)

macht, weil sein Mei - ster ein Schu - ster!
cause he gets strapped when he's naugh-ty!

Bei'm Leisten sitzt er mit der
He cobbles with a goose's

gut!
well!

DAV. (setzt sich in Positur.)
(poses himself.)

Mässig bewegt.

marcato
fp
stacc.
cresc.
più f -
Mein
Sir

Herr! Der Singer Meister-schlag gewinnt sich nicht an einem Tag.
Knight! The Master-singer's seat needs more than one short day to get.
In Nüremberg der
For full a year our

grösste Mei-ster mich lehrt die Kunst Hans Sachs; schon voll ein Jahr mich unterweist er
greatest Master has taught me art, ah me! un-less my steps go rather faster,

poco cresc.
f *dim.*

dass ich als Schü - - - - - - - ler wachs'.
ne'er shall I scho - - - - - - - lar be.

Schuhmacherei und Po-e-te-rei, die lern' ich da all-ei-ner-lei;
Shoe-maker's craft and po-et's art both dai-ly I learn by heart;

hab'ich das Le-der glatt ge-schlagen, lern'ich Vo-cal und Consonnanz sa-gen;
first all the lea-ther smooth I hammer, con-sonants then and vowels I stammer;

wichst'ich den Draht erst fest und steif, was sich dann reimt, ich wohl be-greif'.
next must the thread be stiff with wax, then I must learn, it rhymes with Sachs.

Den Pfriemen schwingend, im Stich die Ahl', was stumpf, was
With awl and thread I make stitch-es neat, and then I

klin-gend, was Maas, was Zahl,— den Lei-sten im Schurz, was lang, was
learn a-bout time and beat— with lap-stone and last, the slow, the

kurz, was hart, was lind, hell o-der blind, was Wai-sen was Myl-ben, was Kleb-
fast, the hard, the light, gloom-y and bright, the scissors and snippings, and word-

syl-ben, was Pau-sen, was Kör-ner, was Blu-men, was Dör-ner,— das
clippings, the pau-ses and corns, the flowers and thorns, I

al-les lernt'ich mit Sorg' und Acht: wie weit nun, meint ihr, dass ich's ge-
learn all such things with care and pains: to what now think you all this at-

WALTH.

Wohl zu'nem Paar recht gu - ter Schuh?
Say, to a pair of right good shoon?

DAV.

bracht?
tains?

DAV.

Ja, da'- hin hat's noch gu - te Ruh! Ein „Bar" hat manch' Gesätz' und Ge-
Ah, think not that is reached so soon! A "Bar" of ma - ny stan-zas is

bänd': wer da gleich die rech-te Re - gel fänd', die richt' - ge Nath und den
made: and the rules a-lone would break your head, and right - ly stitched and

rech - ten Drath, mit gut ge-füg - ten Stol - len den Bar recht zu-ver-
tru - ly pitched must words and mu - sic an - swer, when bar is soled with

DAV.

soh - len! Und dann erst kommt der Ab-gesang, dass der nicht kurz und nicht zu lang, und auch
stan-za! *Then com-eth first the After-song, and not too short nor yet too long; and in*

kei - nen Reim ___ ent - hält, ___ der schon im Stollen ge -
it ___ no rhyme ___ may sound ___ that in the stan-za is

stellt. Wer al-les das merkt, weiss und kennt, wird doch immer noch nicht
found, *Who all this has read, marked and learned hath e'en yet the name of*

WALTH. **Schneller.**

Hilf Gott! Will ich denn Schu-ster sein?
Odd's life! Teach me not cobbler's trade?

Mei - ster ge - nennt.
Mas - ter not earned.
Schneller.

WALTH.

In die Singkunst   lie-ber führ'mich ein!
Rather tell me   how a singer's made!

DAV.

Ja— hätt' ich's nur selbst schon zumSinger ge-
Ah, would that a sing-er al-ready I

dolce

p

p

bracht! Wer   glaubt wohl, was das für Mü-he   macht!
were! Who   know-eth what time that needs and   care!

tranq.   dolce

cresc. — — sf   f dim.   p

Der Mei — — ster Tön' und Wei — — — sen, gar viel an
The Mas — — ters' tones and mea — — — sures are ma-ny in.

p

Nam' und Zahl,   die star — ken, und die lei — — sen, wer die wüss-te
name and kind;   the strong ones and the soft ___ ones, who at once their

f   *p*

dolce

f   *p*

P.   ✛   P.   ✛

27327

DAV.

Re - gen-bo-gen, die Nach - - - ti-gal-weis'; die englische Zinn, die Zimmtröhren
rain-bow mode and the night - - - in-gale mode; the English tin, the cin - namon

Mässig.

dolciss.

weis', frisch Po-me - ran-zen, grün Lin-den-blüh - weis'; die Frösch', die
mode, fresh po-me - granates, green lin-den bloom mode; the frog, the

rall. a tempo

dolce

rall. a tempo

poco riten.

Käl - ber, die Stie - glitzweis', die ab-ge-schied'ne Viel - frassweis', der
calf,___ the lin - net mode; the lonely gor-mandi - zer mode, the

poco riten. Mässig.

Ler - chen, der Schnecken, der Bel-ler-ton; die Me-lis-sen-blüm-lein, die
sky - lark, the snail, the barking tone; and the honey-flow-er, the

cresc.

dim.

DAV.

klingen, wo steigt die Stimm', und wo sie fällt; fangt nicht zu hoch, zu tief nicht an, als es die
ringing, as voice doth rise and fall at need; start not too high, too low in pitch, but where the

Stimm' er-rei-chen kann. Mit dem A-them spart, dass er nicht
voice all notes can reach. To the breath give heed and hold it

knappt und gar am End' ihr ü-berschnappt; vor dem Wort mit der Stim-me ja nicht
well, lest at the end your voice should fail. Ere a word you pronounce, make not a

summt, nach dem Wort mit dem Mund auch nicht brummt. Nicht än-dert an
groan, when the word ends, the voice may not moan; and al-ter not

DAV. (greinend) / (weeping)

weiss, sing' ich die ei-tel Brod und Was-ser-weis! Nehmt
gain I sing a-lone the bread and wat-er-strain. Then

Tempo primo. poco riten. a tempo.

euch ein Bei-spiel d'ran,_____ und lasst vom Mei-ster-
heed this les-son well;_____ be-ware the Mas-ter

wahn!_____ Denn Sin-ger und Dich-ter müsst ihr
spell!_____ Till sing-er and po-et he has

sein, eh' ihr zum Mei - - - - -ster keh-ret
been, no one the Mas - - - - -ter's crown can

(Hörner marc.)

DAVID.

füg-tet ihr selbst nun Reim' und Wort; dass sie ge-nau an Stell' und Ort pass-ten
if you yourself both rhyme and word find and unite in true ac-cord, so that

p

dolce

zu ei-nes Mei-sters Ton: dann trägt ihr den Dich - - ter-preis da -
they fit some Master's tone: then you've made the Po - - et's prize your

cresc. - -

f

von.
own.

ALT.

1ͬ TENOR.

He! Da-vid! soll man's dem Mei - ster kla-gen? Wirst' dich
Hey! Da-vid! must we then tell thy master? Wilt thou

2ͬ TENOR.

Soll man's kla - gen?
Shall we tell him

ff (lärmend)

f f f

P.

LEHRBUBEN.
PRENTICES.

wieder umkehrend.)
quickly back.)
(mit sehr tiefsinniger Miene)
(in a very solemn manner)
mit, Herr Ritter, ist's so bewandt: Der Dichter, der aus eig'nem
Knight, that title we thus assign: The poet who by rules as
p
dolce
(äusserst zart)
(dolcissimo)
Fleisse, zu Wort' und Reimen, die er erfand, aus
stated, to words and rhymes he himself has found, can
p dolce
rall.
a tempo
Tönen auch fügt eine neue Weise:
fit a new strain by himself created
f
der wird als „Meister-
shall then as "Master-
Gewichtig.
fp
cresc.

64

27327

66

(Die Lehrbuben, welche in der Mitte der Bühne ein grosses Gerüste mit Vorhängen aufgeschlagen hatten, schaffen auf Davids Weisung dies schnell bei Seite, und stellen dafür ebenso eilig ein geringeres Bretter- gerüst auf; darauf stellen sie einen Stuhl, mit einem kleinen Pult davor, daneben eine grosse schwarze Tafel, daran die Kreide am Faden aufgehängt wird; um das Gerüst sind schwarze Vorhänge angebracht welche zunächst hinten und an den beiden Seiten, dann auch vorn ganz zusammengezogen werden.)

(The Prentices, who had put up a large erection with curtains in the middle of the stage, put it aside under David's directions and substitute for it a smaller stage; on this they place a chair with a small desk before it, near it a large black board on which a piece of chalk is hung by a string; around the stage are hung black curtains which are pulled together first at the back and sides and then in front.)

27327

67

27327

DAV.

— man-cher Wer-ber ver-sang.
ma-ny can-di-dates fail.
Sie — ben
Se — ven

Feh-ler giebt er euch vor,_ die merkt er mit Krei-de dort an:
faults the Marker lets by,— with chalk they are marked on his slate:
wer ü — ber
if more than

sie-ben Feh — ler ver-lor, hat ver-sun-gen und ganz ver-than!
se-ven faults he should spy, then the sing-er has met his fate!

(derb in die Hände schlagend.)
(clapping his hands loudly.)

Nun nehmt euch in Acht:_ der Mer-ker wacht!
Good heed must you take:_ his ear's a-wake!
Glück
God

molto cresc.

27327

(zusammen)

cresc.

LEHRBUBEN.
PRENTICES.

Blu-menkränzlein aus Sei-den fein, wird das dem Herrn Ritter be - schie-den sein,___
silk-en chaplet of flowers bright, will that by good fortune be yours, sir knight___

cresc.

Blu-menkränzlein aus Sei-den fein, wird das dem Herrn Ritter be-schie-den sein,___
silk-en chaplet of flowers bright, will that by good fortune be yours, sir knight___

cresc.

Blu-menkränzlein aus Sei-den fein, wird das dem Herrn Ritter be-schie-den sein,___
silk-en chaplet of flowers bright, will that by good fortune be yours, sir knight___

p

stacc.

poco a poco cresc.

più

aus Sei - - - den fein, das
of flow - - - ers bright the

più

aus Sei - - - den fein, das
of flow - - - ers bright the

più

aus Sei - - - den fein, das
of flow - - - ers bright the

più f

Dritte Scene.

(Die Einrichtung ist nun folgender Massen beendigt: — zur Seite rechts sind gepolsterte Bänke in der Weise aufgestellt, dass sie einen schwachen Halbkreis nach der Mitte zu bilden. Am Ende der Bänke, in der Mitte der Bühne, befindet sich das „Gemerk" benannte Gerüste, welches zuvor hergerichtet worden. Zur linken Seite steht nur der erhöhte, kathederartige Stuhl („der Singstuhl") der Versammlung gegenüber. Im Hintergrunde, dem grossen Vorhang entlang, steht eine lange Bank für die Lehrlinge. — Walther verdriesslich über das Gespött der Knaben, hat sich auf die vordere Bank niedergelassen. Pogner ist mit Beckmesser im Gespräch aus der Sakristei aufgetreten. Die Lehrbuben harren ehrerbietig vor der hintern Bank stehend. Nur David stellt sich anfänglich am Eingang der Sakristei auf.)

Third Scene.

(*The arrangement of the stage is now thus completed; on the right stuffed benches are placed in a curve facing the centre. At the end of the benches, in the middle of the stage is the "Gemerk" (the marker's stage) which has been erected. On the left stands a high ecclesiastical chair (the "singing chair") opposite the benches. At the back in front of the great curtain stands a long bench for the pupils. — Walther, vexed with the boys' mocking, has seated himself on the front bench. Pogner has come from the sacristy in conversation with Beckmesser. The prentices stund waiting respectfully before the back bench. Only David takes his place at first by the sacristy door.*)

POGNER.

Mässig (♩ ein wenig langsamer als zuvor ♩.)

(zu Beckmesser.)
(to Beckmesser.)

Seid mei-ner
Be well as-

Treu-e wohl ver-se-hen, was ich be-stimmt, ist euch zu Nutz: im
sured of my good favour; what I have planned will serve you well: suc-

Wett-gesang müsst ihr be-ste-hen, wer bö-te euch als Meis-ter Trutz?
cess will go with your en-deavour; who wields like you the mas-ter's spell?

BECKM.

Doch wollt' ihr von dem Punkt nicht weichen, der mich ich sag's be-denk-lich macht: kann
Yet will you not that point pass o-ver, where on, in truth, I'm doubtful still: if

Ev'chens Wunsch den Wer-ber strei-chen, was nützt mir mei-ne Meis-ter
E-va's whim may choose her lov-er, what booteth all my mas-ter

POG.

Ei sagt, ich mein; vor al-len Din-gen sollt' euch an dem ge-le-gen
But yet, me-seems your first be-gin-ning should be to find how well you

pracht?
skill?

poco cresc.

sein? Könnt ihr der Toch-ter Wunsch nicht zwin-gen, wie mög-tet ihr wohl um sie
stand; for if her heart you fail in win-ning, how then can you de-sire her

mf   *p*   *più p*

POG.

frei'n?
hand?
BECKM.

Ei ja! Gar wohl! d'rum e-ben bitt ich, dass bei dem Kind ihr für mich sprecht, wie ich ge-
Ah yes! 'tis true! I therefore pray you that with the child you help my love: that I am

p   cresc.   p   poco cresc.

Das thu' ich
With right good

wor-ben zart und sit-tig, und wie Beckmesser grad'euch recht.
soft and tender, say you, and that Beckmesser you ap-prove.

f   p   p dolce

WALTH. (der, als er Pogner gewahrt, aufgestanden und ihm ent-
(who on seeing Pogner has risen and come to meet him,

Ge-stat-tet,
Your par-don

gern.
will.

(Bei Seite.)   Er lässt nicht nach.   Wie wehrt' ich da 'nem Un-ge-mach?
(aside.)   He won't give way.   How to a-void mis-for-tune, say?

p

WALTH.

mich nach Nürnberg trieb, war nur zur Kunst die Lieb'.
home to Nürnberg town was love of art a - lone.

ver-gass' ich's ges-tern Euch zu sa - gen,
Though yes-ter - day I failed to name it,

heut' muss ich's laut zu kün - den wa - gen, ein
now, in this place I dare pro - claim it; a

Meis - ter-sin - ger möcht ich sein!
Mas - ter-sing - er would I be!

WALTH. (sehr innig.)
(cordially.)

Schliesst, Meis-ter, in die Zunft mich ein!
Pray, of your guild now make me free!

(Kunz Vogelgesang und Conrad
Nachtigal sind eingetreten.)
(Enter Kunz Vogelgesang and
Conrad Nachtigal.)

POG. (freudig zu den Hinzutretenden
(turning joyfully to the new

Kunz
Kunz

mf dim. p

p

P.

sich wendend.)
comers.)

Vo - gel-gesang! Freund Nachti - gal! Hört doch, welch ganz be - sond'- rer
Vo - gel-gesang! Friend Nachti - gal! Hear now this passing strange e -

Fall: der Rit-ter hier, mir wohl be - kannt, hat der
vent: this no - ble knight, to me well known, to our

p

poco cresc.

P.

POG.

(Vorstellungen und Begrüssungen: andre Meistersinger treten
(Introductions and greetings: other Mastersingers come forward.)

Meisterkunst sich zu - ge-wandt.
Mas-ter art his thought has bent.

BECKM. (wieder in den Vordergrund tretend, für sich.)
(coming again to the front, aside.)

Noch such ich's zu wenden; doch sollt's nicht ge-
A-gain I will ask him, and if I suc-

noch dazu.)

lingen, versuch' ich des Mädchens Herz zu er-singen; in stil-ler Nacht, von ihr nur ge-
ceed not, then straight will I try if my song she heed not. I'll sing at night to her ears a-

(Walther erblickend.)
(seeing Walther.)

hört, erfahr ich, ob auf mein Lied____ sie schwört.____ Wer ist der Mensch?
lone: perchance by singing may she____ be won.____ What man is that?

POG. (sehr warm zu Walther fortfahrend.)
(continuing very warmly to Walther.)

Glaubt, wie mich's freut! Die al - te Zeit dünkt mich er-
Glad is my heart! The an - cient time is come a-

27327

POGNER.

neu't.   Was   ihr be - gehrt,   so viel an mir,   sei's Euch ge-
gain.   What   you de - sire,   were't mine to grant,   you might com-

BECKM.

Er gefällt mir nicht!   Was will er hier?   Wie der Blick ihm lacht!
I mislike the man!   What would he here?   With his laughing looks.

cresc.   p   dolce

währt. Half ich euch gern bei des Gut's Verkauf,   in die Zunft nun nehm'ich euch gleich gern
mand. Free - ly I helped you your land to sell,   to our guild I wel-come you now as

Holla Six-tus!
Holla Six-tus!

cresc.   f   dim.

P.

WALTH.

Habt   Dank   der Gü-te   aus tief - stem Ge-
My   thanks   now truly   from heart's depth I

auf.
well.

Auf den hab'Acht!
of him be-ware!

p   f   p

27327   P.

WALTH.

mü - the! Und darf ich denn hoffen? Steht heut mir noch of - fen, zu
give you. In this great en-deavour, then may I be-lieve you? The

wer - - ben um den Preis,___ dass Meis - - -
prize I too may gain,___ if Mas - - -

- ter - sin - ger ich heiss'?
- *ter's rank I at - tain?*

POGNER.

Herr
Sir

BECKM.

O - ho! Fein sacht! Auf dem Kopf steht kein
Ah, not too fast! Then the knight's on his

POGN.

Rit - ter, dies geh' nun nach der Re - gel. Doch heut ist Freiung, ich schlag' euch
Wal - ther, such things by rule we set - tle. To-day is Tri-al, but have no

Kegel!__
mettle!

(Die Meistersinger sind nun alle angelangt, zu-
letzt auch Hans Sachs.)
(All the masters have now arrived, Hans Sachs last.)

vor, mir lei - hen die Meis - ter ein wil - lig Ohr.
fear; I gain from the mas - ters a will-ing ear.

VOGELGESANG.

HANS SACHS.
Sind wir bei - sammen?
Are all to - gether?

BECKM.
Gott grüss' euch, Meister!
God greet you, Masters!

NACHTIGAL.
Der Sachs' ist ja da!
Yes, Sachs too, is here!

So ruft die
Let names be

poco a poco cresc.__

27327

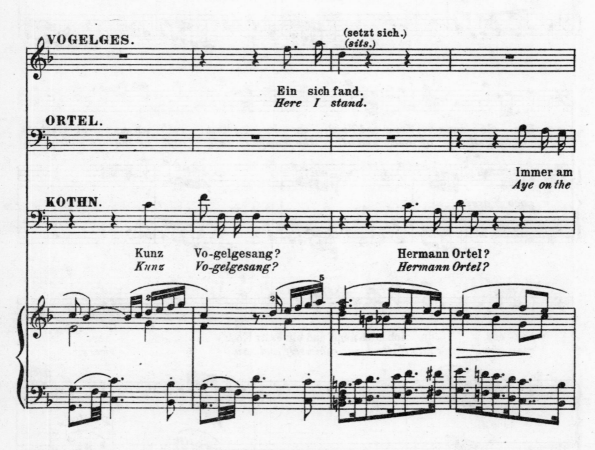

88

LEHRBUB. (Altist.) (von der Bank aufstehend.)
PRENTICE. (rising from his seat.)
(er setzt sich wieder nieder.)
(he sits down again.)
Ist krank!
Is ill!
Schön Dank!
His thanks!
VOGELGESANG.
Walt's Gott!
A - men!
ZORN.
Walt's Gott!
A - men!
MOSER.
Walt's Gott!
A - men!
POGNER.
Walt's Gott!
A - men!
ORTEL.
Walt's Gott!
A - men!
NACHTIGAL.
Walt's Gott!
A - men!
KOTHNER.
Schweigt?
Speaks not?
Gut' Bess'rung dem Meister!
Good health to the Master!
Hans
Hans
cantabile
f
dim.
p

90

27327

92

POGN.

Tanz im Lust-ge - lag, an fro-her Brust ge-bor-gen, ver-ges-sen sei-ner
dance a-mong the hay, with heart filled full___ of gladness, for-get-ting all his

poco cresc.

P.

Sor-gen, ein Je - der freut sich, wie er mag. Die Singschul' ernst im Kirchen-
sad-ness, let each re-joice as best he may. To raise the so-lemn chant on

poco f

dim.

P. P.

chor die Meister selbst ver - tau-schen, mit Kling und Klang hinaus zum Thor, auf off'-ne
high, our singing school we bor - row: through gate and door, with shout and cry, to o - pen

p

P. P.

Wie - se ziehn sie vor, bei hel-len Fes - tes Rauschen das Volk sie las-sen
mea-dows all will hie: while there each one re-joi-ces, for ears unlearned our

poco a poco cresc.

P.

POGN.

lauschen dem Freigesang mit Lai-en Ohr.
voi-ces a master-song shall raise on high.

Zu ei-nem Werb-und
When gifts are won in

Wett-ge-sang ge-stellt sind Sie-ges — preise,
strife of song that blithely swells and ri-ses,

und bei-de preist man
then ac-cla-ma-tions

weit und lang', die Ga — be wie die Wei-se.
loud and long will greet both songs and pri-zes.

Nun
As

schuf mich Gott zum rei-chen Mann;
God hath made me passing rich,

und giebt ein Je-der, wie er kann, so muss-te ich wohl
and wealth its duties lays on each, I sought a-mong my

27327

POGN.

sin-nen, was ich gäb' zu ge - win-nen, dass ich nicht käm' zu Schand'; so
treasure a gift of good-ly measure, lest I to shame be brought; and

cresc.

f

hört denn, was ich fand.
found then what I sought.

Im Zeitmass.

p *molto cresc.* *piú f* *ff dim.*

In deutschen Landen viel gereis't, hat oft es mich verdrossen, dass man den Bürger wenig
In German lands where-e'er I came, my ears were oft of-fended, hearing our burghers, to our

p

preis't, ihn karg nennt und verschlossen.
shame, as mi-sers re-pre-hended.

An Hö-fen, wie an nied'rer
In castle as in humble

cresc. *f* *p*

POGN.

Statt, des bitt'ren Ta-dels ward' ich satt, dass nur auf Schacher und Geld, sein Merk der Bür-ger
cot, this bit-ter slander ceas-ed not_ that on-ly treasure and gold the burghers dreams can
etwas lebhafter.

cresc.

f

stellt! Dass wir im wei—-ten deut-schen Reich die
hold! That in our em—-pire's spa-cious bounds our

Wieder ruhig.

dim.

p

Kunst ein-zig noch pfle-gen, d'ran dünkt ih-nen we-nig ge-
art we a-lone have tend-ed, me-seems, though 'tis lit-tle com-

P.

p

le-gen. Doch wie uns das zur Eh-re ge-reich', und dass mit ho-hem
mended, yet to our burgh-ers' hon-our re-dounds. And that in stead-fast

poco cresc. -

P.

POGN.

Muth wir schät - zen, was schön und gut,
mood, *we* *trea - sure the* *fair and good,*

was werth___ die Kunst, und was sie gilt, das ward ich der Welt zu
the pow'r___ of art and all its worth___ to that I would fain bear

zei-gen gewillt, d'rum hört, Meis - ter, die Gab', die als Preis bestimmt ich
witness on earth: this gift, then, I choose as prize: may ye Mas - ters deem it

hab'! Dem Sin - - - ger, der im
wise! *To him___ whose song a-*

POGN.

Kunst-ge-sang vor al - - lem Volk den Preis er-rang,
mong the rest, in o - - pen strife ye judge the best,

am Sankt Jo-han-nis - tag, sei er wer er auch mag, dem geb'
on John the Baptist's day, be he who-e'er he may, then will

ich, ein Kunst-ge-wog'ner, von Nü-renberg, Veit Pogner, mit all meinem
I, as art's de-fender, with all my goods sur-render the dear - est

Gut, wie's geh' und steh', E-va, mein ein-zig Kind, zur
trea - sure of my life__ E - va, my on-ly child, for

MEISTER.
MASTERS.

Da sieht man, was ein Nürn - ber - ger
He speaks as none but Nürn - ber - gers

Mann!
man!

Da sieht man, was ein Nürn - ber - ger
He speaks as none but Nürn - ber - gers

Mann!
man!

Da sieht man, was ein Nürnber - ger
He speaks as none but Nürnber - gers

sieht man, was ein Nürn - ber - ger kann! D'rob
speaks as none but Nürn - ber - gers can! There-

P.

P.

kann!
can!

D'rob preist man euch noch weit und
There - fore our prais - es, far and

kann!
can!

D'rob preist man euch noch weit und
There - fore our prais - es, far and

kann!
can!

D'rob preist man euch noch weit und breit, den
There - fore our praises, far and wide shall

preist man euch noch weit und breit, euch den wack' - ren
fore our praises, far and wide, aye shall sound a -

POGNER.

zunft;
guild;
doch gilt's der Eh',
but maid-ens' hearts
so will's Ver-
may not be

dolce

nunft,
willed;
dass ob der Meis- - ter Rath
whom-e'er the Mas- - ters choose,
die
the

cresc.

P.

KOTHN.

Versteh' ich
I un-der-

BECKM. (zu Kothner gewandt.)
(turning to Kothner.)

Dünkt euch das klug?
Doth that seem wise?

Braut den Aus- - schlag hat.
bride may still re- -fuse.

P.

KOTHN.

gut,   ihr gebt uns in des Mägdlein's Huth?
stand, you place us in the maid-en's hand?

Stimmt es nicht
Must we a-

BECKM.

Gefähr-lich das!
That were not safe!

bei, wie wä-re   dann der Meister Ur-theil frei?
gree? Who then could call the Masters' judgment free?

BECKM.

Lasst's gleich wählen nach Herzens-
Whom she loves let her heart pro-

ziel,   und lasst den Meister-ge-sang aus dem Spiel!
claim,   and leave the mas-ter-song out of the game!

POGNER.

Nicht so! Wie doch? Versteht mich
Not so! How now? Hear me a-

POGNER.

recht! | Wen ihr Meis - ter den Preis zu -
right! | *If your judg - ment on one should*

sprecht, die Maid _____ kann dem ver her
light who fails _____ *to gain her*

weh - ren, doch nie ei-nen and'-ren be - gehren. Ein
fa - vour, un - wed-ded she lives then for e - ver. A

Meis - - ter-singer muss er sein, nur wen ihr krönt,
Mas - - ter-singer must he be: he whom ye crown,

Etwas breiter. *Noch breiter werdend.*

SACHS (erhebt sich.)
(rises.)

POGNER.

Ver - zeicht, vielleicht schon
One word! perchance al -

den soll sie frei'n.
and none but he!

Früheres Zeitmass.

ginget ihr zu weit. Ein Mäd - chenherz und Meis - ter-
ready ye have erred. A maid-en's dreams and our ___ de-

kunst erglüh'n nicht stets in glei - cher Brunst: der Frau - en
sires gain not their glow from self - same fires; and wo - man's

Sinn, gar un - be - lehrt, dünkt mich dem Sinn des Volk's gleich werth.
mind, in art un-taught, seems to the folk's a - like in thought.

27327

108

27327

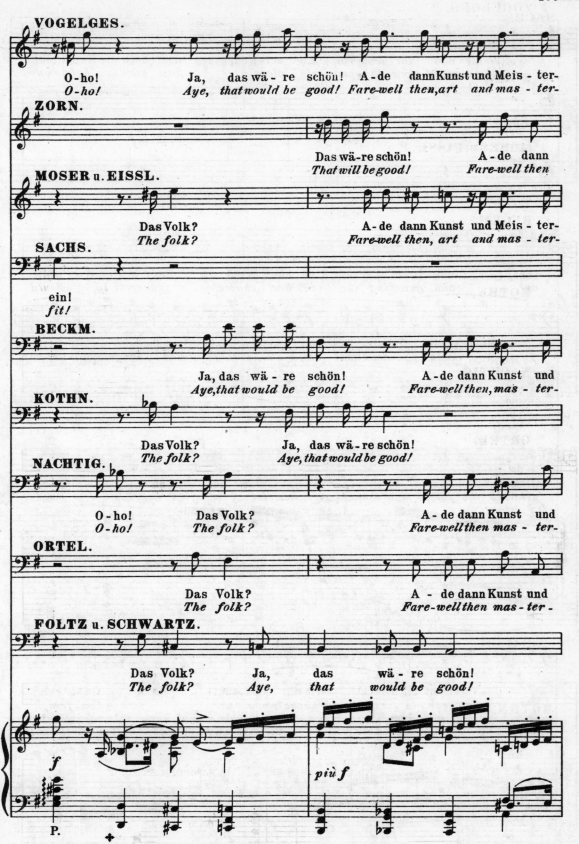

VOGELGES.

tön'!
hood!

ZORN.

Kunst!
art!

MOSER u. **EISSL.**

tön'!
hood!

BECKM.

Tön'!
hood!

KOTHN.

Nein, Sachs! Ge-wiss, das hat keinen Sinn! Gäb't ihr dem Volk die Re-geln
Nay, Sachs! in-deed that plan has no sense. Ruled by the folk, all art goes

NACHTIG.

Tön'!
hood!

ORTEL.

Tön'!
hood!

stacc.

fp   cresc. —   —   *f*

P.

SACHS.

Vernehmt mich recht! Wie ihr doch thut! Ge - steht,
Nay hear a - right! Why chafe you so? Con - fess,

KOTHN.

hin?
hence?

stacc.

p tr   *f*   *sf*   *p*   cresc. —   —

P.   +   P.   +

27327

SACHS.

wohnheit trä - gem Glei - se ihr Kraft und Le -
tame in custom's teth - er, their force and life

- ben nicht sich verlier'! Und ob ihr der Na -
should dwin - dle and die! And if on na - ture's

tur noch seid auf rech - ter Spur, das sagt euch nur,
road your feet have firm - ly trod, they know for sure

(Die Lehrbuben springen auf und reiben sich
die Hände.)
(The prentices spring up and rub their hands.)

wer nichts weiss von der Ta - bu - la - tur.
who nought know of the Ta - bu - la - ture.

27327

SACHS.

liesst es selbst euch auch sa - gen, ob das ihm zur Lust ge- to
lay be - fore them the mat - ter, and ask what seems best to

schah. Dass Volk und Kunst gleich blüh und wachs',
them. That folk and art shall bloom and wax,

cresc. — f dim. cresc.

bestellt ihr so, mein' ich, Hans Sachs!
if this ye do, think I, Hans Sachs!

f > > > dim. p cantabile poco cresc. — —

VOGELGES.

Ihr meint's wohl recht!
You mean right well.

KOTHN.

Doch steht's d'rum faul.
And yet 'tis wrong.

NACHTIG.

Wann spricht das Volk, halt ich das
If mobs may speak I hold my

cresc. — tr —

115

27827

117

27327

SACHS.

sein,   soll Ev-chen ihm den Preis ver - leih'n.
prove, when E - va's heart bestows her love.

BECKM.

Als wie auch ich?__ Gro-ber Ge-
Than I, you say?   Ill-mannered

sell'
boor!

KOTHNER.

Begehrt wer Frei-ung, der komm' zur Stell'! Ist Jemand gemeld't, der Freiung be-
Who comes a - wooing? be not a-fraid! Is an-y one here who wishes to

gehrt?
wed?

POGNER.

Wohl, Meister,   zur Ta-gesordnung kehrt, und nehmt von mir Be-
Now Masters,   the or-der of the   day! And hear from me this

27827

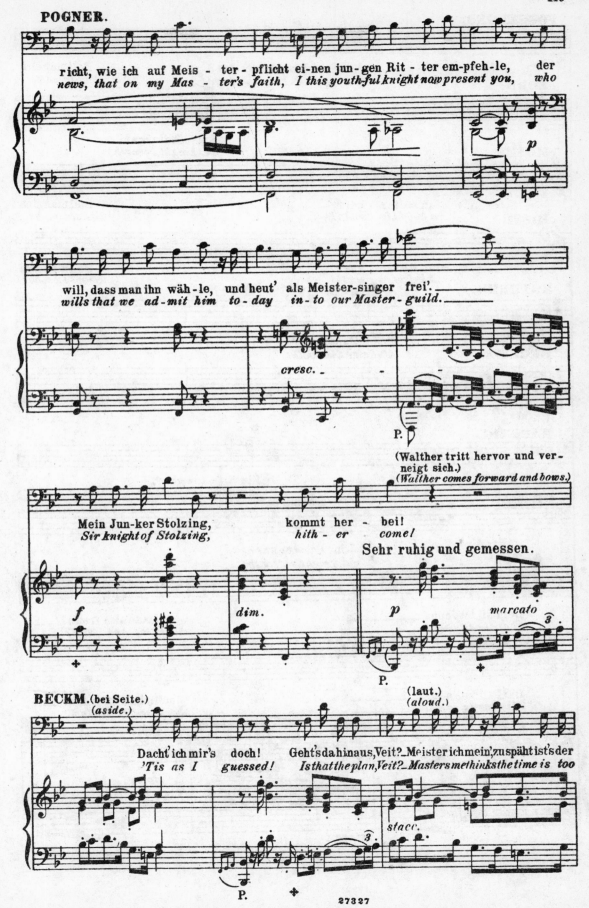

120

27327

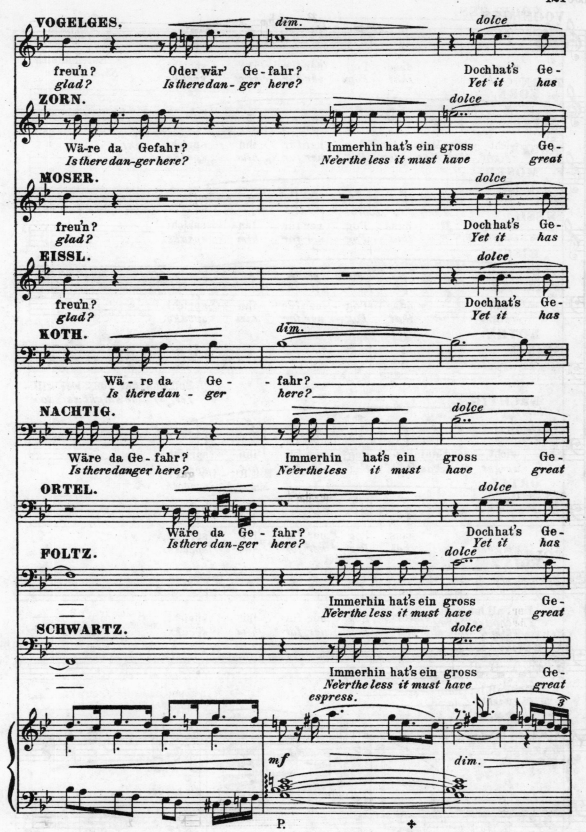

KOTHNER.

kommen sein,   zu-vor muss er wohl   ver - nom-men sein.
join our guild,   he first must be tried   and   du - ly passed.

POGNER.

Vernehmt mich wohl!
Mistake me not!

Wünsch' ich ihm Glück, nicht bleib' ich doch hin-ter der Re-gel zu-rück.   Thut, Meister, die
Friend though he be,   yet   I desire nought that the rules do not grant.   Put, Masters, the

p

KOTHNER.

So mög' uns der Junker   sa - gen: ist er frei und ehrlich ge-
So now let the knight first tell us: are his birth and standing ap-

Fragen.
questions.

poco cresc.   mf   f   p

KOTHNER.

bo - ren?
proved?

POGNER.

Die Fra - ge gebt ver - loren, da ich euch selbst dess' Bürge steh', dass er aus
That question I will answer, for, as his sure - ty here I stand, that he is

frei' und ed - ler Eh': Von Stol - zing Wal - ther aus Franken-
free and no - bly born: the knight of Stol - zing in Franken-

f dim. p poco cresc. -
P. marcato

land, nach Brief und Ur - kund mir wohl be - kannt. Als seines
land, by fame and let - ters to me well known. Sole living

Stammes letz - ter Spross verliess er neu - lich Hof und
sci - on of his race, of late he left his cas - tle

poco cresc.

P.

27327

schlossen ist, ob Herr und Bauer, hier nichts beschiesst: hier frägt sich's nach der Kunst al-
made of old, that lord and peasant a-like we hold: here nought is prized but art a-

lein, wer will ein Meister-sin-ger sein.
lone, in those who seek the Master's crown.

KOTHNER.

D'rum nun frag' ich zur Stell': welch'
Then his an-swer I claim: his

Meister's seid ihr Ge - sell'?
Mas-ter now let him name.

Noch mehr zurückhaltend.

WALTH.

Am stillen Herd in Winters-zeit, wann Burg und Hof mir ein-ge-
In snowbound hall by fire side, when prisoned fast at winter-

Mässig.

27327

130

27327

KOTH.

fort? Mich dünkt, der Jun - ker ist fehl__ am Ort.
halt? Me - thinks the knight is e'en now__ at fault.

SACHS.

Das wird sich bäld - lich zei - gen: wenn rechte Kunst ihm ei - gen, und
We must not judge too light-ly if art has led him right-ly; if

gut__ er sie be-währt, was gilt's, wer sie ihm ge-lehrt?
well__ he sings by rule, what matters master or school?

KOTH. (zu Walther.)
(to Walther.)

Seid ihr be - reit, ob euch ge - rieth__ mit neu - er
Are you prepared to show this throng, if you have

KOTH.

Find' ein Meisterlied, nach Dicht' und Weis' eur' ei-gen, zur Stunde jetzt zu
found a Mastersong with words and tune well mated, and by your-self cre-

zei - gen?
a - - ted?

WALTH

Was
The

Win-ter-nacht, was Waldes-pracht, was Buch und Hain mich wie - sen, was
se-cret deep of winter's sleep, of woods in summer's glo - ry. the

Dichter-san - ges Wunder-macht mir heimlich wollt' er schlies - sen; was
hid-den word of book and bird, revealed in po-et's sto - - ry; the

WALTH.

ei - nig mir es flies - sen, als Meister - sang, ob
geth - - er sweet - ly ma - ted; a Master - song, if

den ich weiss, euch Meis - tern sich er - gies - - - -
for-tune speed, by me shall be cre - a - - - - -

sen.
ted.

BECKM.

Ent - nahmt ihr 'was der Wor - te
What sense is in the whirl-ing

dem Gemerke zu.)
the "Gemerk")
BECKM.

(Er verneigt sich gegen
Walther.)
(He bows towards Wal-
ther.)

mal!
trow!

Wohl giebt's mit der Krei-de man-che Qual!
The chalk will be bu - sy, well I know!

Herr Rit - ter, wisst: Six-tus Beck-mes-ser Mer - ker
Sir Knight, give ear: Six-tus Beck-mes-ser mark-eth

ist; hier im Ge-merk' ver-rich-tet er still sein strenges
here: Here will he lurk and si-lent-ly do his cru-el

Werk.
work.

Sie - ben Feh - ler giebt er euch
Se - ven faults he let-teth pass

BECKM.

vor,
by,
die merkt er mit Krei - de dort an:_ wenn er
with chalk they are marked on the slate:_ but if

ü - ber sie-ben Feh - ler ver - lor,
more than seven faults he should spy,
dann ver -
then, Sir

(Ersetzt sich im Gemerk.)
(He sits in the Gemerk)

sang der Herr Rittersmann.
Knight, you have met your fate.
Gar fein er hört; doch dass er
His ears are keen; but, lest your

euch den Muth nicht stört,
soul, if he were seen,
säh't ihr ihm zu, so giebt er euch
should be dis - tressed, he leaves you at

BECKM.

(Er streckt den Kopf, höhnisch freundlich nickend
(*He puts out his head with a mocking friendly*

Ruh', und schliesst sich gar hier ein,— lässt Gott euch be-foh-len
rest, and hides him-self a - way:— God grant you his grace to-

più p   *pp*   *dim.*

P.

heraus, und verschwindet hinter dem zugezogenen Vorhange des Gemerkes gänzlich.)
nod, and then disappears behind the drawn curtains of the "Gemerk!")

KOTH. (winkt den Lehrbuben.)
(*beckons to the prentices.*)

sein. *day.*

più p   *ppp*   *meno p*   *cresc.*

u.c.   *t.c.*

KOTH. (zu Walther.)
(*to Walther.*)

Was euch zum Lie - de Richt' und Schnur, ver-nehmt nun aus der Ta - bu-la -
These rules to make your foot-steps sure, now hear you from the ta - bu-la -

p   *cresc.*

(Die Lehrbuben haben die an der Wand aufgehängte Tafel der „Leges Tabulaturae" herabgenomen,
(*The prentices have taken down from the wall the board of the "Leges Tabulaturae" and*

tur! *ture!*

f schwer   *f*   *f*   *f*   *f*

sehr markirt.

und halten sie Kothner vor; dieser liest daraus.)
hold it before Kothner who reads from it.)
(lesend)
(*reading*) **sehr markirt.**

KOTH.

Ein je - des Meister-gesanges   Bar stell' ordentlich ein Gemäs-se
A song hath "bars," as the Masters teach, which duly present a measure

dar   aus un - terschiedlichen Ge - sätzen, die Kei-ner soll ver-letz -
each: for this are sundry stanzas   needed, with laws that must be heed -

en.
ed.

Ein Ge-sätz be-
In a stan-za

steht aus zweenen Stollen, die glei-che Me - lo - dei ha-ben sollen; der Stoll'aus et-li-cher
strophes two are mated: one tune for these must then be cre-ated: each must to se-veral

KOTH.

Vers' Ge-bänd, der Vers hat ei-nen Reim am___ End'___
lines ex-tend, each line or verse a rhyme must___ end___

Da-rauf er-folgt der Abgesang, der sei auch et-lich' Ver-se
There follows then the aftersong, which is se-veral verses

lang und hab' sein' be-sond're Me-lo-dei, als nicht im Stol-len zu fin-den
long. This al-so must have its me-lo-dy, the which must not in the strophe

sei___ :
be___ :

Der-
The

144

27327

WALTH.

Hall von dan - nen flieht, von weit-her naht ein Schwel - len, das
reached its farth-est bound, when distant glens re - ply - - ing gave

mäch - tig nä - her zieht. Es schwillt und schallt, es
back a might-y sound. The woods ere long are

tönt der Wald von hol - der Stimmen Ge-men - ge; nun
filled with song and sweet-ly clamour-ous voi - ces; now

laut und hell, schon nah' zur Stell', wie wächst der Schwall! Wie
loud and clear the sound draws near; the tu - mult swells like

WALTH.

Glo-cken-hall er-tos't des Ju-bels Ge-drän-ge! Der
peal-ing bells, and ev'-ry creature re-joic-es! All

Wald,_____ wie bald ant-wor-tet er dem
heard_____ spring's word, and, an-swer-ing her com-

Ruf, der neu ihm Le-ben schuf:
mand, that woke the sleep-ing land,

stimm-te an das süs-se Len-zes-
raised on high the ten-der song of

Ossia.

WALTH.(Man hört aus dem Gemerk unmuthige Seufzer des Merkers, und heftiges Anstreichen
mit der Kreide._ Auch Walther hat es gehört; nach kurzer Störung fährt er fort.)
(*From the "Gemerk" are heard Marker's sighs of illhumour and vigourous scratching
of the chalk; Walther hears it too, and, after a few moments of discomposure, continues.*)

lied.
spring.

In ei - ner Dornen - he - cken, von Neid und Gram ver - zehrt musst'
Deep hid in thorny co - ver, con-sumed by wrath and hate, when

er sich da ver-stecken, der Winter Grimm be-wehrt: von dür-rem Laub um -
now his reign is o - ver, old Winter lies in wait: in gloom of deep-est

rauscht, er lauert da und lauscht, wie er das fro - he Sin-gen zu
woods he cow-ers there and broods how all this singing's gladness his

cantabile

WALTH.

Traum; mein Herz mit be - ben-den Schlä - gen er -
thrilled, the blood in tur - bu - lence stream - - ing, my

füllt - te des Bu - sens Raum: das Blut, es wällt mit
bo - som with rap - ture filled: my pul - ses beat with

All - ge-walt, ge-schwellt von neuem Ge-füh - le; aus
ar - - dent heat of un - known feel - ings throng - ing; through

war - mer Nacht, mit Ue - ber-macht, schwillt mir zum Meer der
sul - try night, with po - tent might, tempests of sighs in

WALTH.

Seuf - zer Heer in wil - dem Wonne Ge-wüh - le Die
tu - mult rise and tell my passion of long-ing; I

Brust, wie bald ant - wor-tet sie dem
heard spring's word and, answer-ing her be -

Ruf, der neu ihr Le - ben schuf;
hest that woke my sleep-ing breast,

stimmt nun an das heh - re Lie - bes-
raised on high the glorious song of

Oder.

WALTH.

Er - laubt _____ ihr's, Mei - ster, dass er mich
I ask _____ you, Mas - ters, is this not

BECKM.

schwört!
word!

Hob. & Clar.

stört?
wrong?

Blieb' ich von Al - - - - len unge-
May no-one hear _____ me end my

hört?
song?

BECKM.

POG.

Sei
Be

Ein Wort, Herr Mer - ker! Ihr seid ge - reizt.
One word, Sir Mark-er! Not too much zeal!

BECKM.

Mer - ker fort - an, wer dar - nach - geizt.
Mark - er hence-forth who - e - ver will.

Doch dass der
But, that the

Jun - ker hier versungen hat, be - leg' ich erst noch vor der Mei-ster Rath.
knight who sang is all unskilled, that will I prove to all the master's guild.

Zwar wird's
'Faith, hea -

— 'ne har-te Ar - beit sein: wo be - ginnen, da wo nicht aus noch
- vy toil the task will be! Where be - gin it, when sense no man can

ein?
see?

Von falscher Zahl und falschem Ge-bänd'— schweig' ich
False beat and feet, without a - ny law:— phra - ses

BECKM.
schon ganz und gar: zu kurz, zu lang' wer ein End'da fänd'? Wer
too short, too long: no form, no plan, ne'er an end I saw! Who

meint hier im Ernst ei-nen Bar? Auf „blin-de Meinung" klag'ich al-lein.
calls that in earn-est a song? His "ha-zy meaning," that is e-nough.

MOSER.
Man ward nicht
I found no

BECKM.
Sagt, konnt' ein Sinn un-sinniger sein?
Say now, what sense find ye in the stuff?

NACHT.
Ein En-de
None there could

ORTEL.
Ich muss ge-steh'n,____
I must con-fess____

FOLTZ.
Man ward nicht klug; ein End'____
I found no sense, no end____

SCHWARTZ.
Man ward nicht klug' ich
I found no sense, I

poco cresc.

27827

156

27327

BECKM.

kreis' aus „A - benteuer," „blau Rittersporn"Weis', „hoch Tannen,"— „stolz
showed of "bold adventure""blue *rider-spur" mode,"high firtree"— "proud*

Jüng - ling"=Ton!   Kein Ab-satz
strip - ling" tone!   *No pause at*

KOTH.

Ja, ich verstand gar___ nichts da-von.
I un-derstood nought, I must own.

(Die Meister sind im wachsenden Aufstand begriffen.)
(The Masters become more
and more excited.)

wo, kein Co - lo-ra-tur, von Me-lo - dei auch nicht ei-ne Spur!
all, no col-our or grace, of me-lo - dy not e-ven a trace!

ORTEL.

Wer nennt das Ge-
Who calls that a

27327

SACHS.

fest___ und un-be-irrt. Wollt ihr nach Re-geln mes-sen, was
firm *and did not halt.* *If ye by rules would measure* *what*

mf *dim.* *p* *1 2*

allmählich etwas bewegter.

nicht nach eu-rer Re - geln Lauf, der eig'- nen Spur ver-
doth not with your rules___ a - gree; *for - get-ting all your*

allmählich etwas bewegter.

poco a poco cresc. - - -

lebhaft, wie zuvor.

ges-sen, sucht da - von erst die Re - geln auf!
learning, *seek ye first what its rules may be.*

BECKM.

A - ha, schon recht! Nun
A - ha, 'tis well! *Now*

lebhaft, wie zuvor. *3*

f *p* *fp* *f*

P. ✛ P. ✛

hört ihr's doch: den Stüm - pern öff - net Sachs ein Loch, da
hear him, pray! *For bung - lers Sachs re - veals a way,* *where*

3 *3* *3*

fp *f* *fp* *f* *fp* *f*

3 *3* *3*

P. ✛ P. ✛ P. ✛ P. ✛ P. ✛ P. ✛

27327

BECKM.

aus und ein nach Be - lie - ben ihr We - sen leicht sie trie - ben!
they may roam at their plea-sure, with none to take their measure!

Sin - get dem Volk auf Markt und Gas - sen! Hier wird nach den Re - geln nur einge-
Though with their cries the streets are ring-ing, here singers are proved by the laws of

SACHS.

Herr Mer-ker, was doch solch ein Ei - fer? Was doch so we - nig
Sir Marker, why so hot - ly burn-ing? What is it wakes your

las - sen.
sing - ing.

Ruh'! Eu'r Ur-theil, dünkt mich wä - re rei-fer hör'-tet ihr bes-ser zu. Da-
spleen? Your mind, methinks, were more discerning, guided by ears more keen. And

poco cresc.

rum so komm' ich jetzt zum Schluss, dass den Jun-ker man zu End'
so, now hear my fin - al word, that the singer to the end

hö - ren muss. Ver-
must be heard. Now

BECKM.

Die Meister Zunft, die ganze Schul', ge-gen den Sachs da sind wir Null!
The Masters' guild and all the schools, set against Sachs are nought but fools!

hüt' es Gott, was ich be - gehr', dass das nicht nach den Geset - zen wär'! Doch
God for - bid that I should claim to flout our laws or to thwart their aim! But

da nun steht ge-schrieben: „Der Mer-ker wer - de so be - stellt, dass
they speak in this fashion: "The Marker shall be cho - sen so, that,

we-der Hass noch Lie-ben das Ur-theil trü - be, das er fällt."
free from hate and passion, he shall not swerve for friend or foe."

27327

P.

163

27327

BECKM.

Ei! Was kümmert doch Meister
Ei! What is it to Mas-ter

POG.

KOTH.

Ver-mei-det, Meister, Zwist und Streit!
I pray you, Masters, cease this jar!

sön - lich-keit!
wrath be - ware!

più f

ff stacc.

p

P.

P.

Sach - sen auf was für Füs-sen ich geh'?
Sachs, then, how I may see fit to go?

Liess' er drob lie-ber
Let him rath-er give

sfp

f

p

P.

P.

Sor-ge sich wach-sen, dass mir nichts drück' die Zeh'!
heed to his cob-bling, nought then will pinch my toe!

Doch seit mein
But since my

sf

f

P.

Schu-ster ein grosser Po - et, gar ü - bel es um mein Schuhwerk steht:
cob-bler a po-et has been, such shoes he makes as yet ne'er were seen:

fp

fp

(Sachs kratzt sich hinter den Ohren.)
(Sachs scratches behind his ear.)

SACHS.

Ihr mahnt mich da gar recht, doch
Your taunt comes not a - miss, but,
etwas mässiger.

schickt sich's Mei-ster, sprecht, dass find' ich selbst dem E - sel-trei-ber ein
Mas - ters, tell me this: I write on soles of don-key-drivers some
Ruhig.

Sprüchlein auf die Sohl', dem hoch-gelahrten Herrn Stadtschreiber ich nichts drauf schreiben
wis - dom from my hoard; were't fit our learned Sir Town-wri-ter should go with-out a

soll? Das Sprüchlein, das eu'r wür-dig sei, mit all' mei-ner ar-men Po-e-te-
word? But words with worthy wis-dom fraught, a-mong my poor ver-ses long have I

Lebhaft. (wie zuvor)

rei, fand ich noch nicht zur Stund! Doch wird's wohl jetzt mir
sought, yet I found not the right! But now they come in
Lebhaft.

belebend.

27327

27327

(Die Lehrbuben sind von der Bank aufgestanden und nähern sich dem Gemerk, um welches sie einen Ring schliessen und sich zum Reigen ordnen.)
(The Prentices have risen from the bench and form a ring round the "Gemerk," preparing to dance.)

183

(Walther verlässt mit einer stolz verächtlichen Gebärde den Stuhl und wendet sich rasch zum Fortgehen.-
Alles geht in grosser Aufregung auseinander; lustiger Tumult der Lehrbuben, welche sich des Gemerkes,
des Singstuhl's und der Meisterbänke bemächtigen, wodurch Gedränge und Durcheinander der nach dem
Ausgange sich wendenden Meister entsteht.)

(Walther, with a proudly contemptuous gesture leaves the chair and quickly turns to go. General excitement, merry tumult of the prentices who arm themselves-with pieces of the Gemerk, the seat and the benches, causing confusion among the masters who are making for the door.)

P.

(Sachs, der allein im Vordergrunde geblieben, blickt noch gedankenvoll nach dem leeren Singstuhl; als die Lehrbuben auch diesen erfassen, und Sachs darob mit humoristisch unmuthiger Gebärde sich abwendet, fällt der Vorhang.)

(Sachs, who has remained alone in front, still gazes thoughtfully at the empty singer's chair. As the boys remove this, and Sachs turns away with a humourously indignant gesture, the curtain falls.)

Ende des ersten Aufzuges.
End of the first act.

27327

Zweiter Aufzug.
Second Act.

Lebhaft, doch nicht zu schnell.

Der Vorhang geht auf. *The Curtain rises.*

Erste Scene.

Die Bühne stellt im Vordergrund eine Strasse im Längendurchschnitt dar, welche in der Mitte von einer schmalen Gasse, nach dem Hintergrunde zu krumm abbiegend, durchschnitten wird, so dass sich im Front zwei Eckhäuser darbieten, von denen das eine, reichere, rechts —das Haus Pogner's, das andere, einfachere, links das des Sachs ist. Vor Pogner's Haus eine Linde, vor dem Sachsen's ein Fliederbaum. —Heiterer Sommerabend; im Verlaufe der ersten Auftritte allmählich einbrechende Nacht. David ist darüber her, die Fensterläden nach der Gasse zu von aussen zu schliessen. Alle Lehrbuben thun das Gleiche bei andern Häusern.

First scene.

The front of the stage represents a street in longitudinal section, intersected in the middle by a narrow, crooked alley winding towards the back; of the two corner houses thus presented in front, the grander one on the right is Pogner's, the other, simpler one, is Sachs's. Before Pogner's house is a lime tree, before Sachs's an elder.
A genial summer evening; in the course of the first scene night gradually falls.
David is engaged in closing from without the shutters of the windows towards the alley. All the Prentices do the same for other houses.

*) Der Sinn dieser Vortragsbezeichnung ist, dass die Lehrbuben zuerst die Stimme der Magdalene nachahmen, beim Anschwellen aber den natürlichen groben Knabenton hervortreten lassen.

+) From this place the Prentices mimic the voice of Magdalene, but as the tone swells the coarser timbre of the boys voices is heard.

27327

194

MAGD

(Erschrocken.)
(Alarmed.)

Versungen? Ver-
Rejected? No

DAVID.

Lene!   Da steht's bitter: der hat ver-sungen und ganz verthan!
Lene,   that went badly: he was re-ject-ed, all hope is gone.

(Den Korb, nach welchem David die Hand ausstreckt, heftig zurückziehend.)
(Violently pulling back the basket towards which David has stretched out his hand.)

than?   Hand von derTaschen! Nichts zu naschen!   Hilf
hope?   Hands from the basket! Nought for supper!   A -

Was geht's euch nur an?
What is that to thee?

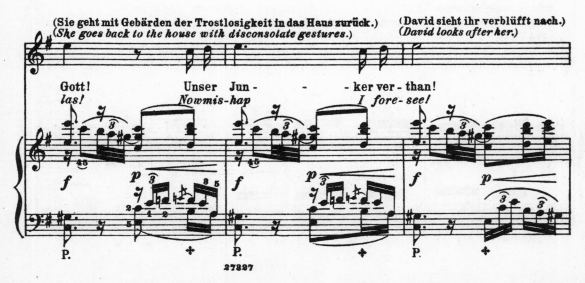

(Sie geht mit Gebärden der Trostlosigkeit in das Haus zurück.)   (David sieht ihr verblüfft nach.)
(She goes back to the house with disconsolate gestures.)   (David looks after her.)

Gott!   Unser Jun -   - ker ver - than!
las!   Now mis-hap   I fore-see!

DAVID.

Schand-lieder singen die!
they all were mocking me!

SACHS.

Hör' nicht d'rauf;
Heed them not;

lern's besser wie sie!
learn better than they!

Zur
Go

Die Lehrbuben zerstreuen sich.
The prentices disperse themselves.

Ruh', in's Haus!
in, lock up!

Schliess', und mach' Licht!
Bring me a light!

DAVID.

Hab' ich heut Singstund?
Have I to sing now?

SACHS.

Nein, singst nicht—
No, not now,

zur Straf' für dein
because that to-

heutig' frech Erdreisten!
day thou hast displeased me!

Die neuen Schuh'
Now put the shoes

steck mir auf den
on the lasts and

27327

Zweite Scene.
(Pogner und Eva, wie vom Spazier-
Second scene.
(Pogner and Eva, returning from

(David und Sachs sind in die Werkstatt eingetreten
und gehen durch eine innere Thüre ab.)
SACHS. (David and Sachs have entered the workshop and go
off through an inner door.)

Leisten!
leave me!

Sehr gemächlich.

gange heimkehrend,—die Tochter leicht am Arme des Vaters eingehenkt, sind beide schweigsam die
Gasse heraufgekommen.)
a walk, have come in silence up the alley, the daughter lightly hanging on her father's arm.)

POGNER (durch eine Klinze im Fensterladen Sachsen's spähend.)
(peeping through a chink in Sachs's shutter.)

Lass seh'n,
We'll see

(David kommt mit Licht aus der Kammer, setzt sich
damit an den Werktisch am Fenster, und macht sich
über die Arbeit her.)
(David comes from the inner room with a light, sits
at the work-bench by the window and works.)

ob Meister Sachs zu Haus?   Gern spräch' ich ihn: trät' ich wohl ein?
if Mas-ter Sachs is there.   I'd   speak with him: shall I go   in?

EVA.   (spähend.)
(peeping.)

Er scheint da-heim: kommt Licht her-aus.
He seems   at home: his light shines out.

POGN.

(Er wendet sich ab.)
(He turns away.)

Thu' ich's?   Zu was doch?   Besser nein.   Will Ei - ner Selt'nes
Shall I?   *Where-for then?*   *Better not.*   *On ways un-wonted*

Mässig.

pp   *cresc.*   *sf*   *dim.*   *p*

wagen, was liess' er sich dann sa-gen?   War
moving, what man can brook re - proving?   *And*

p dolce

er's nicht, der meint', ich ging' zu weit?   Und, blieb ich nicht im Ge-
he 'twas who thought I went too far?   *Yet, though old customs not*

espress.   *cresc.*   *f*   *p*

P. ✦

leise, war's nicht auf sei - ne Wei - se?__   Doch war's vielleicht auch
heeding, I followed so his leading?   *Yet still perchance some*

cresc. -   *dim.*   *più p*

(Sie setzt sich zögernd und beklommen Pogner zur Seite.)
(She sits beside Pogner hesitating and anxious.)

POGN.

Sehr mässig.

Nicht doch, 's ist mild und la - bend, gar lieb - lich lind der
Ah no, the air is kindly, and soft the night and

A - bend: das deu - tet auf den schönsten Tag, der mor - gen soll er -
friend - ly: 'tis pro - mise that the fair - est day to - mor - row will be

schei - - nen. O Kind! Sagt dir kein Herzensschlag, welch'
bring - - ing. O child! Says not thy heart to thee, what

Glück dich morgen tref - fen mag, — wenn Nü - renberg, die gan - ze
joy to - morrow thine may be, — when Nü - remberg in all her

27327

POGN.

Stadt, mit Bürgern und Ge-mei - nen, mit Zünften, Volk und hohem Rath vor
state, 'mid ac-cla-mations ring-ing, will come, with folk both small and great, to

cresc.

dir sich soll ver-ei - nen, dass du den Preis, das ed - le Reis, er-
see thee crown our sing-ing, and thou as bride shalt stand beside the

f   più f   sf   dim.   p dolce

P.   P.

thei - lest als Ge-mahl dem Meister dei - ner Wahl?
man who gains her voice, a Master of thy choice?

cresc.   ff

P.   P.   P.   P.

EVA.

Lieb' Vater, muss es ein Meister sein?
Dear father, Mas-ter, then, must he be?

POGN.

Hör'
But

dim.   più p

P.   P.   P.

27327

EVA.

Lieb' Vä-terchen, komm'! Geh', kleid' dich um.
Dear fa-ther, now come! Go change thy dress. (Während er in's Haus vorangeht.)
(As he goes on before her into the house.)

POGN.

Hm! Was geht mir im Kopf doch
Hm! What thought in my head goes

Blieb still und stumm.
No word he spoke.

(erschrocken.)
(alarmed.)

Der Rit-ter? Hilf
Sir Walther? Ah

MAGD. (heimlich zu Eva.)
(secretly to Eva.)

Hast was heraus?
What hast thou heard?

Sprach Da-vid, meint', er ha-be verthan.
My Da-vid says, the knight is undone.

'rum?
round?

Gott! Was fang' ich an? Ach, Le-ne, die Angst! Wo was er-fah-ren?
me! What shall I do? Ah, Le-ne, the fear! How to dis-co-ver?

Vielleicht von
Perchance from

dim. p

27827

EVA.

(Sie geht in das Haus. Magdalene folgt ihr.)
(*She goes into the house. Magdalene follows her.*)

sein!
that!

SACHS.

(Sachs ist in leichter Hauskleidung von innen in die Werkstatt zurückgekommen.
Er wendet sich zu David, der an seinem Werksitze verblieben ist.)
(*Sachs in a light indoor dress has returned from the inner room to the shop.
He turns to David who is still at his bench.*)

Zeig' her, 's ist gut. Dort an die Thür' rück mir
Come here, 'tis well. There at the door put my

Tisch und Schemel her-für. Leg' dich zu Bett', steh' auf bei
stool and ta-ble out-side. Then go to bed, and ear-ly

dolce

DAVID.

(während er den Tisch und Schemel richtet.)
(*as he arranges the bench and stool.*)

Schafft ihr noch Arbeit?
More work this evening?

Zeit: verschlaf die Dummheit, sei morgen gescheit! Kümmert dich das?
rise: sleep off thy fol-ly, to-morrow be wise! What's that to thee?

DAVID.

(für sich.)
(*aside.*)

Was war nur der Le-ne?__ Gott weiss was!__
What was it with Le-ne?__ God knows what!__

27327

SACHS.

sehr zart.

Mir löst er weich die Glie - der, will, dass ich was sa-gen soll.—
Its sweet-ness weighs up-on me; words from out my heart it calls.—

pp

P. P. P. P. P.

sehr leise.

Was gilt's, was ich dir sa-gen kann? Bin gar ein
What boot such words as I can find within my

Etwas gedehnter.

Erstes Zeitmass.

dolce

pp

poco riten.

P.

Lebhafter.

Immer be-

arm ein-fäl-tig' Mann! Soll mir die Ar-beit nicht schmecken, gäb'st Freund, lieber mich
poor un-let-tered mind? When with my work I am wear-y, then, friend, let me go

Lebhafter.

Immer be-

f *p*

p *cresc.*

wegter.

frei, thät besser, das Le - - der zu stre - cken, und liess' al - le Po-ë - te-
free; 'twere better with lea - - ther to plague me, and let all this po-e-try

wegter.

f *f* *f*

SACHS. (Er nimmt heftig und geräuschvoll die Schusterarbeit vor.)
(He begins to work abruptly and noisily.)

rei!
be!

Lebhaft.

(Er lässt wieder ab, lehnt sich von Neuem zurück,
(He leaves off again and leans back in thought.)

und sinnt nach.)

poco rall.

Und doch, 's will halt nicht gehn:—
And still, that strain I hear:—

Sehr mässig.

ich fühl's, und kann's nicht ver - steh'n;— kann's nicht be - halten,— doch auch nicht ver-
I feel, yet no - thing is clear;— can-not forget it,— nor can I en-

SACHS.

rall.

ges-sen: und fass ich es ganz, kann ich's nicht messen! Doch wie wollt' ich auch
fold it: *I measure it not,* *e'en when I hold it!* *Yet what could gauge its*

immer breiter. rall. Sehr breit.

poco a poco cresc. molto cresc.

P.

mes - sen, was un - - er - mess - lich mir schien.
great - ness? *A mea - - sure no mor - tal hath seen:*

Mässig langsam.

f dim. p dolce

P.

Kein' Re - gel woll-te da pas-sen,— und war doch kein Feh-ler
I found no rule that would fit it, *and yet was no fault there -*

pp cresc. - -

drin. Es klang so alt, und war doch so
in. *It sound - ed old* *and yet was new -*

Ein wenig belebend.

pp dolce

P. P. P. P.

27327

neu, — wie Vo - gel-sang im sü - ssen Mai!
born, — like song of birds on blithe May morn!

poco cresc.

p dolce

più p

P.

Wer ihn hört, und wahn - be-thört sän - ge dem Vo - gel
If one heard, and mad - ly dared that song a-gain to

p

p

poco cresc.

P.

P.

nach, dem brächt' es Spott und Schmach.
sing; but scorn and shame'twould bring.

poco accel.

p

poco cresc.

molto cresc.

P.

P.

Sehr breit.

Len - zes Ge-bot, die sü - sse Noth,
Spring-time's be-hest, with - in his breast,

Sehr breit.

die legt' es ihm in die
on heart and voice there was

f

p

f

f dim.

P.

P.

27327

P.

SACHS.

Brust: ... nun sang er, wie er ___
laid: ... then sang he as Nature

Mässig bewegt.

musst'; und wie er musst', so konnt' er's, ___
bade; and to his need the pow - er

das merkt' ich ganz be - son - ders.
was grant - ed from her dow - er.

Etwas belebend.

sehr zart.

Dem Vo - gel, der heut' sang, dem war der
The bird who sang this morn, from Nature's

Mässig.

Schnabel hold ge-wach-sen;
self had learned his singing;
macht' er den Meistern bang, gar wohl ge-fiel er doch Hans
Masters that song may scorn, for aye Hans Sachs will hear it

Vierte Scene.
Fourth Scene.

(Eva ist auf die Strasse getreten, hat sich schüchtern der Werkstatt ge-
(Eva has come into the street and shyly approached Sachs's shop, and now
(Er nimmt mit heitrer Gelassenheit seine Arbeit vor.)
(He resumes his work with cheerful composure.)

Sach-sen!
ring-ing!

pp

nähert, und steht jetzt unvermerkt an der Thüre bei Sachs.)
stands unnoticed by Sachs's door.)

EVA.

Gut'n A - bend, Meister! Noch so
Good eve - ning, Master! Still a -

più p

fleis - sig?
work - ing?
(Sachs fährt angenehm überrascht auf.)
(Sachs starts in agreeable surprise.)

Ei, Kind! Lieb' Evchen! Noch so
Ah child! Sweet Evchen! Still a -
poco rall.
spät? Und doch,
wake? Yet, why
warum so spät noch,
so late awake, well
Mässig.

f   *dim.*   *p dolce*

EVA. Brauf? / *bride?*

Ja! Weiss es die Stadt, Freund Sachs gu - te Gewähr dann
Yes, all the folk know! Friend Sachs good warrant no doubt, can

SACHS. Ei, was! Das weiss die Stadt.
Ah well! All the folk know.

hat! Ich dacht, er wüsst mehr. Ei,
show! I thought he knew more. Ah,

Was soll ich wis-sen?
What should I know, then?

seht doch! Werd'ich's ihm sa-gen müssen? Ich bin wohl recht dumm?
look now! Must I my secret show, then? Am I, then, so dull?

Das sag'ich
I say not

p *dolce*

P. + P. + P.

EVA.

SACHS.

Dann wär't ihr wohl klug?
'Tis you, then, are crafty?

Ihr wisst nichts?
You know naught!

Ihr sagt nichts?
You say naught!

nicht.
that.

Das weiss ich nicht.
I know not that.

EVA.

Ei, Freund Sachs, jetzt merk' ich wahr-lich, Pech ist kein
Ah, friend Sachs, now I see tru-ly, pitch is not

Wachs. Ich hätt' euch für fei-ner ge-halten.
wax. Methought that your cunning was finer.

Kind, beid, Wachs und Pech, bekannt mir
Oh! both wax and pitch right well I

sind: mit Wachs strich ich die seid'nen
know: 'tis wax streng-thens the silk-en

27327

Fä - den, da - mit ich dir die zie-ren Schuh'ge-fasst:
stitch - ing, where - with for thee those dainty shoes I sewed:

heut'
shoes

fass' ich die Schuh'mit dich'ren Dräh-ten,
now are in hand that call for pitch-ing,

da gilt's mit Pech für den derb'ren
to fit a churl on his sto-ny

EVA.

Wer ist denn der? Wohl was recht's?
Who, then, is he? Some-one great?

Gast.
road.

Das mein' ich!
Aye tru - ly!

Ein
A

Mei-ster stolz auf Frei-er's Fuss;
Mas-ter proud who bold-ly woos,

denkt mor-gen zu sie - gen ganz al-
and hopes, too, to win, if honoured

226

27327

EVA.

SACHS.

Wo so ein Meister den Kopf nur hat! Käm'ich zu
Where doth a Master, now keep his eyes? If in his

lein dein Va - ter Rath.
'tis, who grants the prize.

Etwas lebhafter.

euch wohl, fänd'ich's zu Haus'?
head, then must it be crazed!

(trocken.)
(drily.)

Ach ja! Hast Recht:
Ah yes, art right;

Etwas lebhafter.

'sist im Kopf mir kraus.
'tis my head is dazed.

Hab'heut'manch Sorg'und Wirr'er-
To-day my brain was sore per-

EVA.
(wieder näher rückend.)
(again coming nearer.)

Wohl in der Singschul'?'s war heut Ge-bot?
'Twas in the school, then? Will you not tell?

SACHS.

lebt: da mag's dann sein, dass'was d'rin klebt.
plexed, and 'tis not strange if I am vexed.

più p

p

espr.

P. ✛

Ja, Sachs! Das
Ah Sachs! That

Ja, Kind! Ei-ne Frei-ung mach-te mir Noth.
Yes child, at a tri-al all went not well.

p

p

P. ✛

hät-tet ihr gleich soll'n sa-gen, quält' euch dann nicht mit un-nütz-zen
should you at once have told me, lest all my talk should tempt you to

Fra-gen.— Nun sagt, wer war's, der Freiung be-gehrt?
scold me.— Now tell what man your favour be-sought?

p

Etwas lebhafter.

EVA.

kein Mit-tel gäb's, das ihm ge - dieh'?
to give him aid, was there no way?

Sang er so schlecht, so feh - ler voll, dass
Was, then, his song of fault so full that

nichts mehr zum Mei-ster ihm hel-fen soll?
none might de - fend him in all your school?

SACHS.

Immer breiter im Zeitmass.

Mein Kind, für den ist Al - les ver - lo - ren, und
My child, the man who meets such dis - as - ter, no

sempre rall.

Mei - ster wird der in kei - nem Land;
Mas - ter will be in a - ny land.

denn wer als Mei - ster ge -
Who-e'er is born as a

sehr breit.

MAGD.

(vernehmlicher rufend.)
(calling more audibly.)

Der Va - ter ver-
Thy father has

bo - ren, der hat un - ter Mei-stern den schlimmsten Stand.
mas - ter, finds e - ver with Mas-ters the low - est stand.

wieder belebend. *schnell belebend.* *so lebhaft wie vorher.*

27327

EVA (Immer dringender zu Sachs.)
(Still more urgently to Sachs.)

So sagt mir noch an, ob kei-nen der Meis-ter zum Freund er ge-
But say, in the end, if none of the Mäs-ters he won as a

MAGD.

langt.   espress.   f
called.

p

cresc. - -

P.   ❋   P.   ❋   P.   ❋

wann?
friend?

SACHS.

Das wär' nicht ü-bel,   Freund ihm noch sein!
Ah, how could that be?   Friend who might call

molto espress.

mf

P.   P.

ihm, vor dem sich Al-----le   fühl---ten so
him, be-fore whose great---ness   all   felt so

dim. -

P.   ❋ P.   ❋ P.   ❋   P.   ❋ P.   ❋ P.   ❋

klein?_____   Den Jun-ker Hoch-muth,   lasst ihn laufen!
small?_____   His knightly high-ness!   devil take him!

Belebend.

f   fp sempre stacc.   fp

P.   ❋   P.   ❋   P.   P.   ❋

27327

SACHS.

Mag er durch die Welt sich ranfen; was wir er - lernt mit Noth und
Let the bustling world a - wake him. *Shall he then rob and leave us*

Müh', da - bei lasst uns in Ruh' ver - schnau - fen:
bare of what by la - bour we have won us?

hier renn' er uns nichts über'n Hau - fen; sein Glück ihm an - ders wo er -
Here ne - ver shall he over - run us: let for - tune greet him o - ther -

EVA.

(Sie erhebt sich zornig.)
(She rises angrily.)

Ja! an - ders wo
Aye, o - - ther - where

blüh'!
where!

27327

27327

EVA.

Pech, dass'Gott er-barm';
pitch *should do you harm,*

brennt' er's lieber, da würd' er doch warm!
burn it rather, and make yourself warm!

(Sie geht sehr aufgeregt mit Magdalene über die Strasse
(In great excitement she crosses the street with Magdalene,

Sehr lebhaft und schnell.

hinüber, und verweilt in grosser Unruhe unter der Thüre des Hauses.)
and stops awhile, much agitated at the house door.)

(Sachs sieht ihr mit bedeutungs-
(Sachs looks after her, nodding

Allmählich etwas ruhiger.

sehr

vollem Kopfnicken nach.)
his head meaningly.)

SACHS.

Das dacht' ich wohl.
I thought as much,

Nun heisst's schaff'
now help must

ausdrucksvoll.

27827

MAGD.

Fen- ster nei- gen, er will dir was Schö- nes sin- gen und gei- gen, mit
means to bring thee to-night to thy win-dow, when he will sing thee the

dem er dich hofft zu ge -win -nen, das Lied, ob das dir nach Ge- fal- len ge-
song that shall capture both thee and thy love, to find if thou his lay dost ap-

EVA.

Das fehl-te auch noch! Kä- me nur Er!
Must that be borne, too! Would he but come!

rieth. Hast'
prove. Has

molto espress.

(Sie späht aus.)
(She looks out.)

Was soll mir der? (für sich.)
What's he to me? (aside.)

David geseh'n? Ich war zu streng; er wird sich
David been here? I was too hard; now he'll be

27327

EVA.

Siehst du noch nichts?
See'st thou nought yet?

Wär' er's!
He, 'tis!

MAGD.

(thut, als spähe sie.)
(appears to look out.)

grä — men.
pin — ing.

's ist als ob Leut' dort kämen.
It sounds like people coming.

sf > p

cresc. —

p

P.

Nicht eh'r, _____ bis ich
Not yet, _____ un-til

Mach', und komm' jetzt hin-an!
Come, 'tis time to go in!

poco cresc. —

P.

P.

sah' den theu — — sten Mann!
I my lov — — er have seen!

Ich täuschte mich
My ear was de-

sf

p

P.

27827

MAGD.

dort, er war es nicht. Jetzt komm', sonst merkt der Va- -ter die Ge-
ceived, it was not he. Now come, for fear your fa- ther aught should

EVA.

Ach meine Angst!
Ah, how I fear!

schicht'! Auch lass uns be-rathen, wie wir des Beckmessers uns entladen!
guess! Then let us take counsel how we from Beckmesser now may rid us.

(Sie lauscht.)
(She listens.)

Fen-ster gehst du für mich.
win-dow go thou for me.

(für sich.)
(aside.)

Wie? ich? Das machte wohl Da-vid
What? I? How jealous then Da-vid's

MAGD. (zieht die sich sträubende Eva am Arm die Stufen zur Thür hinauf.)
(pulls the resisting Eva up the steps to the house.)

Zeit.
deed.

Hörst du's?
Hear'st thou?

Komm'!
Come!

Dein Ritter ist
thy knight is not

Fünfte Scene.
Fifth Scene.

EVA.

(Sie erblickt Walther.)
(She sees Walther.)

(Walther ist die Gasse heraufgekommen; jetzt biegt er um die Ecke herum.)
(Walther has come up the alley: he now turns the corner.)

Da
There

weit!
there.

Ziemlich lebhaft.

p

molto cresc.

(Sie reisst sich von Magdalene los, und stürzt Walther auf die Strasse entgegen.)
(She tears herself away from Magdalene, and rushes towards Walther.)

ist er!
is he!

(Sie geht eilig in das Haus.)
(She goes hastily into the house.)

Da haben wir's!
Now wit a-lone

Nun heisst's:
can help

ge - scheit!
us out!

ff

f

27327

244

27827

WALTH.

bür-tig: mein Be - gei-stern fand Ver-ach-ten, und ich
name me: all my pas - sion found but scorning, and I
espress.

weiss es, darf nicht trach - - ten nach der Freun - din
know it; vain my yearn - ing for my la - dy's

EVA.

Wie du irrst! Der Freun - din
How thou err'st! her hand shall
Hand.
hand.

Hand, er - theilt nur sie den Preis, wie dei-nen Muth ihr Herz er -
gire the vic-tor's prize a - lone, within thy heart my heart doth
dolce

EVA.

fand,
live,

reicht ___ sie nur dir
thine ___ then shall be

das
the

Reis.
crown.

WALTH.

Ach nein! Du irrst: der Freun-din Hand,
Ah no! Thou err'st: my la-dy's hand,

wär'
e'en

Kei-nem sie er-ko-ren, wie sie des Va-ters Wil-le
though none else should gain it___ if fast thy fa-ther's word doth

band, mir wär' sie doch ver-lo-ren!
stand, ne-ver may I at-tain it!

„Ein
"A

WALTH.

Meis- - - -ter-sin-ger muss es sein; nur___ wen ihr
Mas- - - -ter-sing-er must he be! he___ whom ye

krönt___ den darf sie frei'n!" So sprach er fest-lich zu den
choose,___ and none but he!" The word that he so firm-ly

Herrn; kann nicht zu-rück, möcht' er auch gern!___ Das
spake, though he should wish, he may not break!___ That

e- - ben gab mir Muth: wie un-gewohnt mir Alles
thought my cou-rage fired: how strange all seemed a-round me

WALTH.

dich nun be - schwör' ich, komm' und
what - e'er be - fall me, fly with

sf dim. - - - p
P.

accel.

folg' mir hin - aus! _____
me, then, to - night! _____

accelerando
cresc. - molto cresc. - - - -
P.

Nichts steht zu hoffen; keine Wahl ist offen! Ueberall Meister, wie bö - se
Hope is bereft us; not a choice is left us, nought but dis - asters! Ev'ry-where

Lebhaft.
sehr gestossen.

ff sf p f p f

Geister, seh' ich sich rotten, mich zu ver-spot - - ten:
Masters! There they are flocking round me and mock - - ing:

fp f p cresc. - sf fp

WALTH.

mit den Ge - wer - ken,   aus den Ge - mer - ken, aus al - len E - cken,
ev'ry where judges,   markers with grudges; out from all al - leys

stacc.

auf allen Flecken, seh' ich zu Haufen Meister nur laufen, mit höhnendem Nicken frech   auf dich
making their sallies, crowds of them hustling. Masters are bustling; in jeering gri-maces twist - ing their

sempre stacc.

cresc.   fp   f   fp   f   fp   f

blicken,   in Krei-sen und Rin-geln dich um - zingeln,   näselnd und
faces;   in   circles a - bout thee, so to flout thee;   snuffling and

p cresc.   f   fp

krei - schend zur Braut dich hei - schend,   als Meis - terbuh - le auf dem
screech - ing, thy hand be - seech - ing;   as Mas - ters' play - thing on the

sf   p   sf

WALTH.

Sin - gestuh - - le zit - ternd und be - - bend,
throne they place thee, trem - bling and quak - - ing,

hoch dich er - he - - bend! Und ich er -
there to dis - grace thee! And I must

trüg' es. sollt' es nicht wa - gen, g'rad'aus tüch - tig
bear it, tame - ly at - tend them, dare not fall on

d'rein zu schla - - gen? Ha!
them and rend them? Ha!

(Man hört den starken Ruf
eines Nachtwächterhornes.)
(The loud horn of the Night-
warder is heard.) (Walther hat mit
(Schrei.) (Walther has laid
(Cry.)

NACHTWÄCHTER (auf dem Stierhorne.)
NIGHT-WATCHMAN (on the cow-horn.)

dim.
ff sehr lang.
più f
ff sehr lang.

SACHS(welcher hinter der Ladenthüre dem Gespräche gelauscht, öffnet jetzt bei eingezognen Lampen-
(who has listened to the conversation from behind the door, now withdraws the lamp and opens

NACHTW.

(auf dem Horn.) sehr lang.
(on the horn.) very long.

Ueble Dinge, die ich da
E-vil doings now are in

Lo - bet Gott, den Herrn!
Praise ye God the Lord!

Mässig.

WALTH.

lichte ein wenig mehr.)
the door a little further.)

(hinter der Linde.)
(behind the lime tree.)

Käm'sie nicht
Com-eth she

merk': ei - ne Ent-führung gar im Werk? Aufgepasst! Das darf nicht sein.
hand: flitting of lovers being planned! Now, to watch! That may not be.

dolcissimo

(Eva kommt in Magdalene's Kleidung aus dem Hause.)
(Eva comes in Magdalene's dress out of the house.)

wieder? O, der Pein! Doch ja, sie kommt
not then? Woe is me! Ah yes, she comes

(Eva erblickt Walther, und eilt auf ihn zu.)
(Eva sees Walther and hastens towards him.)

dort?_ Weh' mir!_ nein!_ die Al-te ist's.
there? Woe's me!_ no!_ the old one'tis.

espressivo

Doch_
poco accel. Yet_

poco cresc.

27327

EVA.

Von hinnen! Von hinnen! O wä-ren wir schon fort!
Away now! Away now! Oh, would that we were gone!

WALTH.

Hier durch die Gasse, dort finden wir vor dem
Here through the alley, then. Ready, without the

pp

molto cresc. — — —

P.

(Als sich Beide wenden, um in die Gasse einzubiegen, lässt Sachs,
nachdem er die Lampe hinter eine Glaskugel gestellt, durch die ganz
wieder geöffnete Ladenthüre einen grellen Lichtschein quer über
die Strasse fallen, so dass Eva und Walther sich plötzlich hell be-
leuchtet sehen.)

(As they both turn to go into the alley, Sachs, after placing his lamp be-
hind a glass globe, lets a bright beam of light fall across the alley
through the opened shutter so that Eva and Walther suddenly find
themselves clearly illuminated.)

(Walther hastig zurückziehend.)
(hastily drawing Walther back.)

EVA. Ziemlich belebt.

O weh! Der Schuster! _ Wenn der uns
A-las! The cobbler. _ If he should

Thor Knecht und Rosse vor.
gate, squire and horses wait.

NACHTW.

(auf dem Horn, entfernt.)
(on the horn, at a distance.)

p

Ziemlich belebt.

f   *p.*   *sf*

27327

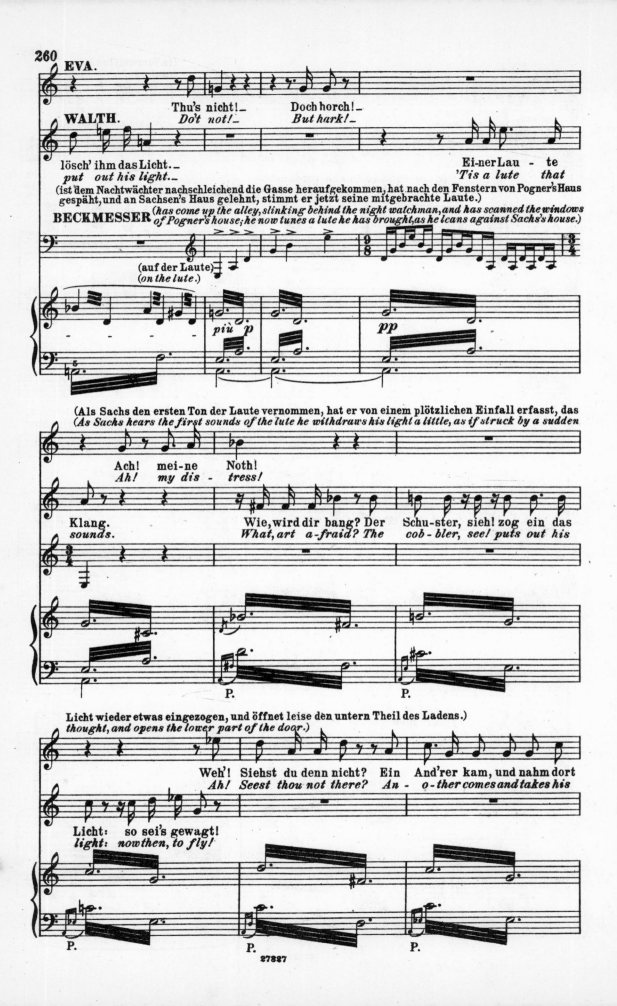

EVA.

WALTH.

Thu's nicht!_ Doch horch!_
Do't not!_ But hark!_

lösch' ihm das Licht._
put out his light._

Ei-ner Lau - te
'Tis a lute that

(ist dem Nachtwächter nachschleichend die Gasse heraufgekommen, hat nach den Fenstern von Pogner's Haus
gespäht, und an Sachsen's Haus gelehnt, stimmt er jetzt seine mitgebrachte Laute.)

BECKMESSER (has come up the alley, slinking behind the night watchman, and has scanned the windows
of Pogner's house; he now tunes a lute he has brought, as he leans against Sachs's house.)

(auf der Laute)
(*on the lute.*)

più p   pp

(Als Sachs den ersten Ton der Laute vernommen, hat er von einem plötzlichen Einfall erfasst, das
(*As Sachs hears the first sounds of the lute he withdraws his light a little, as if struck by a sudden*

Ach! mei-ne Noth!
Ah! my dis - tress!

Klang.
sounds.

Wie, wird dir bang? Der
What, art a-fraid? The

Schu-ster, sieh! zog ein das
cob - bler, see! puts out his

P.   P.

Licht wieder etwas eingezogen, und öffnet leise den untern Theil des Ladens.)
thought, and opens the lower part of the door.)

Weh'! Siehst du denn nicht? Ein
Ah! Seest thou not there? An -

And'rer kam, und nahm dort
o-ther comes and takes his

Licht: so sei's gewagt!
light: now then, to fly!

P.   P.   P.

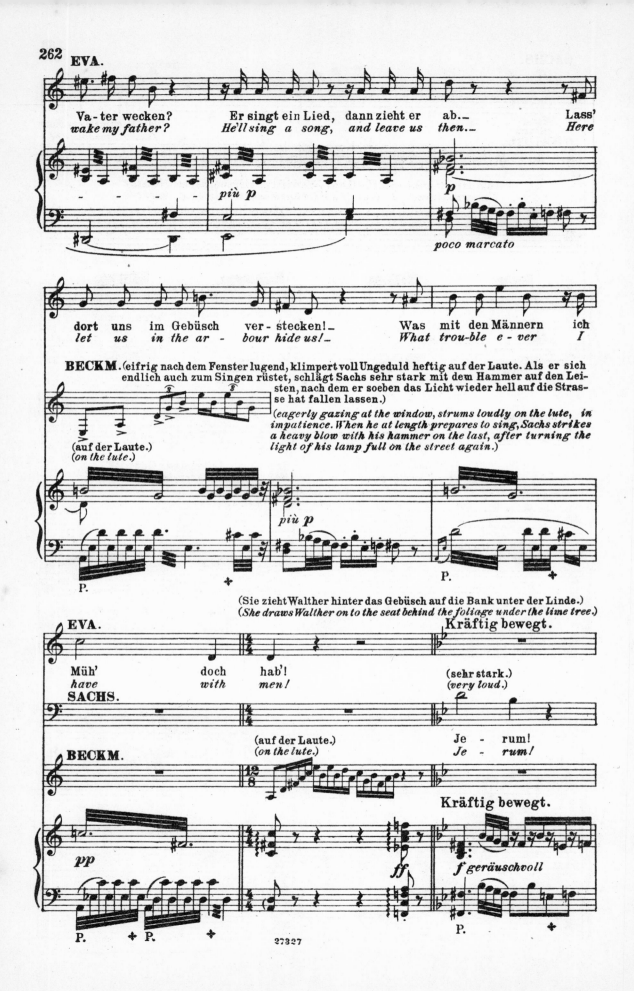

SACHS.

Je - rum!   Hal-la-hal-lo-he!   O - ho!
Je - rum!   *Hal-la-hal-lo-he!*   *O - ho!*

BECKM.

(springt ärgerlich von dem Steinsitz auf, und gewahrt Sachs
(*springs up angrily from the seat and perceives Sachs at work.*)

Trala-lei!   Tra-la-lei!   O - ho! — Als
Trala-lei!   *Tra-la-lei!*   *O - ho!* — *When*

bei der Arbeit.)

Was soll das sein?   Ver-damm-tes Schrei'n!
What can that be?   *Ac-curs - ed noise!*

E - va aus dem Pa - ra - dies von Gott dem Herrn ver - stos - sen, gar
Eve from Pa - ra - dise was cast, her sin she soon re - pent - ed, for,

SACHS.

schuf ihr Schmerz der har - te Kies an ih - rem Fuss, dem blo - - -
toil-ing o'er the sto - ny waste, her feet were sore tor - ment - - -

- - - - - sen.
- - - - - ed.

Das
There-

BECKM.

Was fällt dem groben Schu-ster ein?
What plan is in the cob-bler's head?

EVA.

(flüsternd zu Walther.)
(whispering to Walther.)

Ich hört es schon;'sgeht nicht auf
I heard it well; but 'tis not

WALTH. (flüsternd zu Eva.)
(whispering to Eva.)

Was heisst das Lied? Wie nennt er dich?
What means the song? Thy name I hear.

jammer-te den Herrn,   ihr Füsschen hatt' er gern: und
at the Lord was moved,   her ten-der feet he loved: some

EVA.

mich:
I;

doch ei-ne Bosheit steckt da-rin.
yet malice hidden li - eth there.

SACHS.

sei-nem En-gel rief er zu:
comfort he might not re-fuse;

da mach' der ar-men Sünd'rin Schuh'; und
so bade an an-gel make her shoes. Then,

dolce

P. ✠

WALTH.

Welch' Zögerniss!
Why stay we now?

SACHS.

da der A-dam, wie ich seh', an Stei-nen dort sich stösst die Zeh', das
see-ing A-dam limping tread with feet all torn with stones, he said; though,

cresc.

Die Zeit geht hin!
The time goes by!

(sehr lang.)
(very long.)

recht fortan er wan-delnkann, so miss dem auch Stie - feln an!
truth to tell, in sin he fell, measure him for boots ___ as well.

cresc. -

P. ✠

27327

SACHS.

Je - rum! Hal-la-hal-lo-he! O - ho!

BECKM.

Schuh'! Hier will ich Ruh'!
shoes! Here I want peace!

Tra-la - lei! Tra-la - lei! O he!__

a tempo.

O E - va! E - va! Schlim - mes Weib, das
Oh Eve, on thee this guilt has lain, and

sehr ausdrucksvoll

EVA.

Gu-tes.
e-vil.

Michbetrübt das
'Tis the song that

WALTH.

Mein sü-sser Engel, sei guten Mu-thes!
My sweetest angel, comfortthy spirit!

SACHS.

dies, da gab es kei - nen Kies: um dei - ner jun - gen
found on Eden's ho - ly ground: for that of-fence that

p *p* *cresc.* *p*

P. ✠

Lied.
wounds.

Ich hör' es kaum; du bist bei mir: _____ welch'
I hear it not; thou art by me: _____ what

Mis - se - that hand-thier' ich jetzt mit Ahl' und Draht, und
wrought thy fall, I sit at work with thread and awl, and

p *p*

P. ✠

(Er zieht Eva zärtlich an sich.)
(He draws Eva tenderly to him.)

p

hol - - - der Traum! _____
bliss - - - ful dream! _____

ob Herrn A - dam's üb - ler Schwäch' ver - sohl' ich Schuh' und
eke to pay for A - dam's crime, in sol - ing shoes I

cresc.

P. ✠ P. ✠ P. 27327 ✠ P. ✠

strei - che Pech! Wär' ich nicht fein
spend my time! Were I not, too,
En - gel rein, Teu-fel möch - te Schu -
an - gel true, dev-ils might make shoes
- ster sein! Je - - - -
for you! Je -

BECKM. (drohend auf Sachs zufahrend.)
(coming threateningly towards Sachs.)

(sich unterbrechend.)
(interrupting himself.)

Gleich hö - ret auf! Spielt ihr mir Streich'?
Come to an end! What is this trick?

Bleibt ihr Tag's und Nacht's euch gleich?
Night and day are you the same?

SACHS.

Wenn ich hier sing' was kümmert's euch? Die
If here I sing, what's that to you? And

Schu - he sol-len doch fer - tig werden?
look you! shoes will you need to-morrow!

BECKM.

So schliesst euch ein, und schweigt da-zu
Then hold your peace, and get you with-

Des Nacht's ar - bei - ten
But night shoe - mak-ing

still!
in.

macht Be - schwer - den; wenn ich da mun-ter blei-ben
bring - eth sor - row; to cheer my heart and cure my

SACHS.

Halla-hallo he!
Halla-hallo he!
O ho
O ho
Trala-lei
Trala-lei

BECKM.

Das grobe Ge- schrei!
This infamous noise!

Kl.Fl. in 8ve

P.

Tra-la - lei
Tra-la - lei
O he!
O he!
O
O

riten.
a tempo.

AmEnd' denkt sie gar, dass ich das sei!
At last, she will think 'tis I who sing!

riten.
a tempo.

(Beckmesser hält sich die Ohren zu, und geht verzweiflungsvoll, sich mit sich berathend, die Gasse vor dem Fenster auf und ab.)
(*Beckmesser stops his ears and walks in despair up and down the alley before the window, ruminating.*)

SACHS.

E - va! hör' mein' Kla - ge- ruf, mein' Noth und schwer Ver -
Eve, my woes must wring thy heart, and make us mourn to -

Ob. Cl. Hr. Fg. (sehr ausdrucksvoll.)

f sehr ausdrucksvoll.

27827

SACHS.

drüs - sen! Die Kunst-werk', die ein Schus - ter schuf, sie
ge - - ther! The world con - temns the cob - bler's art and

tritt die Welt mit Füs - - - - - -
treads up - on his lea - - - - - -

- - - sen!
- - - ther!

SACHS.

Gäb' nicht ein En-gel Trost, der glei-ches Werk er-los't, und rief mich oft in's
Were not an an-gel there, to charm a-way my care, to Pa-ra-dise oft

Pa - ra - dies, wie ich da Schuh' und Stie - fel liess! Doch
call - ing me, I soon would let my cob - bling be! But

wenn mich der im Him-mel hält, dann liegt zu Füs - sen
when en - throned in Heaven's seat, the world doth lie be -

mir die Welt, und bin in Ruh' Hans Sachs, ein Schuh -
neath my feet: then, born a - new, I am a shoe -

EVA. (leise.) (softly.)
'S ist Magda-le-ne.
'Tis Magda-le-ne.

WALTH. (leise zu Eva.) (low to Eva.)
Wer ist am Fenster?
Who's at thy window?

BECKM.
hört doch nur ein Wort! Wie seid ihr auf die Schuh' ver-sessen! Ich hatt' sie wahrlich
me but speak a word! Why let the shoes so much dis-tress you. I give my word I'd

WALTH.
Dass heiss ich vergelten. Fast muss ich la-chen.
I call that requital! It moves my laughter.

schon vergessen. Als Schus - ter seid ihr mir wohl werth, als
clean forgot them. As cob - bler, well I know your worth, in

etwas geziert.

p

P.

EVA.
Wie ich ein End' und Flucht mir er - seh-ne!
Would we might fly and end all this trouble!

Kunst - -freund doch weit mehr ver-
art your place is first on

P. P.

27327

279

SACHS.

noch gedehnter.

fassen? Mag mich nicht wie-der schel-ten las-sen. Seit sich der
catch me? *Not a - gain will I let you teach me* *how, since the*

riten.

Schus-ter dünkt Po-et___ gar ü - bel es um eu'r
cob - bler po - et has been, such shoes he makes as ne'er

Allmählich etwas lebhafter.

Schuhwerk steht: ich seh', wie's schlappt und ü - ber - all
yet were seen: un - sound through - out, they flap all a -

stacc.

klappt; d'rum lass' ich Vers und Reim'_____ gar bil - lig
bout! Writ - ing of songs, I swear,_____ for you I

cresc. __ __ sf f p

BECKM.

Herz.
breast.

Vom Volk _____ seid ihr ge-ehrt, auch der Pog-ne-rin seid ihr
The folk _____ all feel your spell, and the maiden, too, loves you

LAUTE.

(wie vorher.)
(as before.)

werth: will ich vor al-ler Welt nun mor-gen um die werben, sagt! ___
well: if I to-morrow came, to win the people's favour, were't

könnt's mich nicht verderben, wenn mein Lied ihm nicht gefällt? D'rum hört mich ruhig an, und
not a vain endeavour, if my song Hans Sachs should blame? Now listen to my song, and

(wie vorher.)
(as before.)

BECKM.

sang ich, sagt mir dann, was euch gefällt, was nicht — dass ich mich darnach richt'!
tell me what is wrong; then, to attain my end, your words my work shall mend!

LAUTE.

poco cresc.

SACHS.

Ei! lasst mich doch in Ruh'; wie kä-me sol-che Ehr'mir zu? Nur Gas - senhauer
Ah, cease and let me be: how could such honour come to me? If nought but doggrel

dicht' ich zum meisten: D'rum sing' ich zur Gas-sen, und hau' auf den
rhymes I can stammer, then dog-grel I sing as my leather I

Leisten! Je - - rum! Je - - rum! Hallo-hallo-he!
hammer! Je - - rum! Je - - rum! Halla-hallo-he!

BECKM.

Verfluch - ter Kerl! Den Verstand ver - lier' ich, mit seinem
Ac-curs - ed rogue! All my sens - es leave me, a-mid his

Lebhafter.

SACHS.

O ho! Trala-lei! Trala-lei! O he!"
O ho! Trala-lei! Trala-lei! O he!

BECKM.

Lied____ voll Pech und Schmie___rich! Schweigt doch! Weckt ihr die
song____ that reeks of black___ing! Si - lence! Folk now to

Die sind's gewöhnt,'s hört keiner d'rauf. „O E-va E-va!____
They know me well; they will sleep on. "O Eve, o Eve, how____

Nachbarn auf?
bed are gone?

BECKM. (In höchste Wuth ausbrechend.)
(In a transport of rage.)

Oh, ihr boshafter Ge - sel-le! Ihr spielt mir heut' den letzten Streich:
Oh, you base, black hearted rascal! More tricks like this you'll play not here!

Sehr lebhaft.

BECKM.

schweigt ihr jetzt nicht auf der Stelle, so denkt ihr d'ran, das schwör' ich euch.
Now at once, silence that howling, or you'll re-pent your trick I swear!

(*Er klimpert wüthend.*)
(*He strums furiously.*)

LAUTE.

Nei - disch seid ihr, nichts weiter: dünkt ihr euch auch gleich ge-
En - vy-cursed were you ever, though you deem yourself so

scheiter; dass And're auch was sind, ärgert euch schändlich: glaubt, ich
clever: that others, too, have wits e - ver en-raged you: through and

Etwas zurückhaltend im Zeitmass.

ken - ne euch aus und in - wendlich! Dass man euch noch nicht zum Merker ge-
through, believe me, I have gauged you. That the post of Marker you cannot

27327

BECKM.

wählt, das ist's, was den gallichten Schuster quält. Nun gut!
win — 'tis that wakes the rancourous cobbler's spleen. Ah well,

Noch mehr zurückhaltend. *Wieder lebhafter.*

So lang' als Beckmesser lebt, und ihm noch ein Reim an den Lippen
so long as Beckmesser sings; while a single rhyme to his lips he

klebt; so lang' ich noch bei den Meistern was gelt',___ ob
brings; so long as I a-mong Mas-ters am famed, though

Nürn - berg blüh' und wachs', das schwör'___ ich Herrn Hans
Nü - remberg bloom and wax, I swear___ to you Hans

Nicht zu schnell.

BECKM.

Sachs, nie wird er je zum Mer - ker be-stellt.
Sachs, ne - ver shall you as Mark - er be named. (Er klimpert in höchster Wuth.)
(He plays in intense fury.)

LAUTE.

Allmählich zurückhaltend.

Der Teufel hol's!
Ill-mannered hound!

SACHS.(der ihm ruhig und aufmerksam zugehört hat.)
(who has listened to him quietly and attentively.)

War das eu'r Lied?
Was that your song?

Mässig.

Zwar wenig
The rules were

Wollt ihr mich hören?
Will you not hear me?

Re - gel, dochklang's recht stolz. In Got-tes
lack - ing, but brave the sound. For Heaven's

27327

SACHS.

ei - nig geht der Mensch am best'.
comrades *bet - ter speed than one.*

Darf ich die
Al - though my.

Ar - beit nichtent-fer - nen,
work brooks no de - ni - al,

dieKunst des Mer-ker's möcht'ich er-
in Mark - er's craft now give me a

ler - nen;
tri - al.

da - rin kommt euch____ nun Kei - ner
In that you have____ no peer, 'tis

gleich: ich lern' sie nie, wennnicht von euch.
true: how learn the art if not from you?

BECKM.

Verdamm-te Bosheit! Gott, und 's wird spät! Am End' mir die Jungfer vom Fenster
Ac-curs-ed malice! God, and 'tis late! and long at the window she will not

SACHS.

richt.
told.

geht!
wait!

Haltet ein! Nur das nicht!
Nay, not that! Be si-lent!

LAUTE. (Er klimpert eifrig.)
(He strums eagerly.)

Fanget an, 's pres-sirt: sonst sing' ich für mich.
Now begin, time flies: or I too shall sing.

(Teufel! wie är-gerlich!) Wollt ihr euch denn als Mer - ker erdreisten,
(Devil now take the thing.) Would you as Marker make a beginning?

(immer wie vorher.)
(as before.)

cresc.   sfp   sfp

BECKM.

nun gut, so merkt mitdemHammeraufden Leisten; nur mit dem Be-
'Tis well; but strike on-ly if youcatchme sinning; yet, be it a-

ding, nach denRe-geln scharf, a-bernichts, was nachden Re - geln ich
greed, by the rules a - lone; do notblame what by the rules may be

BECKM.

darf.
done.

SACHS.

Nachden Re - geln, wie sie der Schu - ster kennt, dem die
On the rules, then, the cobbler takes his stand, thoughhis

Auf Mei-sterehr'?
By Masters'rule?

Ar-beit un-terdenHän - den brennt. Und
work is burning beneath his hand. With

EVA.
(sanft an Walther's Brust gelehnt.)
(leaning softly on Walther's breast.)

Die Schläf'um - webt mir's wie ein
My brain is dazed as by a

WALTH.
Singstuhl, scheint's, ver - liess ichkaum.
am I in the school me-seems.

BECKM.
Euchnicht zu sehen, wie's Brauch der Schul' vor dem Gemerk!
Because the marker, must not be seen; so says the rule.

SACHS.
Warum so weit?
But why so far?

EVA.
Wahn:___ ob's Heil,___ ob Un - heil, was ich
spell:___ if good___ or ill - fate, who can

BECKM.
Der Stim - me Stärk'ich so gar lieb-lich däm - pfen
My voice is full; more sweetly so your ear 'twill

SACHS.
Da hör'ich euch schlecht.
Then I shall not hear.

cresc. mf p dolce
P. + P. +

BECKM.

Bin ganz verwirrt!
I'm all dis-traught!

SACHS.

fort!
time.

So fang't noch 'mal an: drei Schläg' ich jetzt pau -
Be-gin, then, once more: three faults I pass as

(bei Seite)
(aside)

Am besten wenn ich ihn gar nicht be-acht': wenn's nur die Jungfer nicht ir-re macht!
'Twere best to heed not a word he may say. If on-ly she, too, no heed will pay!

si - ren kann.
marked be-fore.

BECKM. (auf der Laute)
(on the lute)

„Den Tag seh' ich er - scheinen, der mir wohl ge-fall'n
"I see now dawning day-light, that gives me de-light

LAUTE.

27327

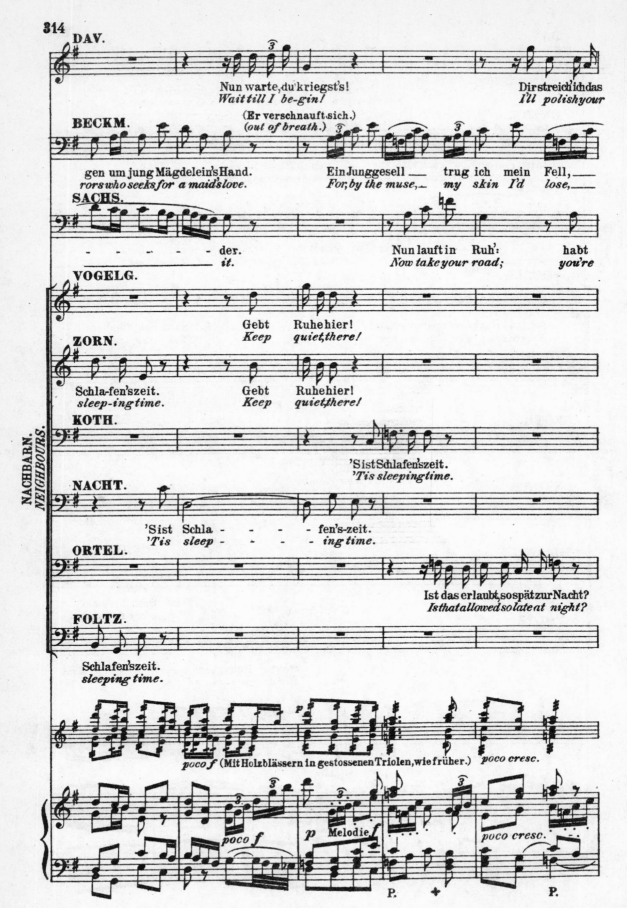

27327

DAV. (Er entfernt sich nach innen.)
(He goes in.)

Fell!
skin!

BECKM.
— mein' Ehr', Amt, Würd' und Brod zur Stell' _____ dass
— my of - fice, rank, the goods I use, _____ that

SACHS.
gu - te Schuh', der Fuss auch d'rin nicht
right - ly shod: these shoes will fit _____ your

VOGELG.
Mein', hört nur, wieder E-sel schreit! Ihr da! seid
Ah, hear but how the donkey brays! You there! be

ZORN.
Mein', hört nur, wieder E-sel schreit!
Ah, hear but how the donkey brays!

KOTH.
Mein', hört nur wie er schreit! _____
Ah, hear but how he brays! _____

NACHBARN.
NEIGHBOURS.

NACHT.

ORTEL

FOLTZ.
Mein', hört nur, wie dort der E - sel schreit! Seid
But on - ly hear how the donkey brays! Be

DAV.

(David ist, mit einem Knüppel bewaffnet, zurück gekommen, Magdalene winkt, da sie David wieder kommen sieht, diesem heftig zurück, was Beckmesser als Zeichen des Missfallens deutend, zur äussersten Verzweiflung im Gesangsausdrucke bringt.)

(*David, armed with a cudgel, comes back. Magdalene, seeing him return, makes urgent signs to him to go away, which Beckmesser interprets as signs of displeasure, and his singing expresses his despair.*)

BECKM.

euch mein Ge- sang wohl ge - fäll', _____ und mich das
you the prize should not re- fuse, _____ *and me the*

SACHS.

knackt, ihn hält die Sohl' _____ im Takt!
feet; *their soles* *will mark* _____ *the beat!*

VOGELG.

still! Ihr da! heult, kreischt und schrei an and'rem Ort!
still! *You there!* *howl, cry and bray some other-where!*

ZORN.

Seid still!
Be still!

KOTH.

Seid still!
Be still!

NACHT.

Seid still, und scheert euch fort!
Be still and get you gone!

ORTEL.

Heult und kreischt __ an and'rem Ort!
Howl and cry ____ some other-where!

FOLTZ.

still und scheert euch fort!
still and get you gone!

sempre

NACHBARN.
NEIGHBOURS.

P.

27327

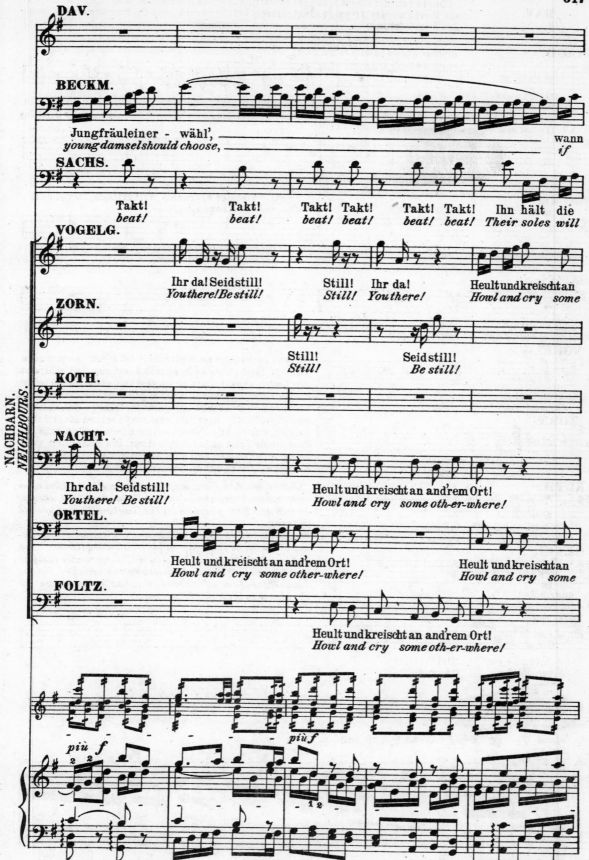

Siebente Scene.
Seventh Scene.

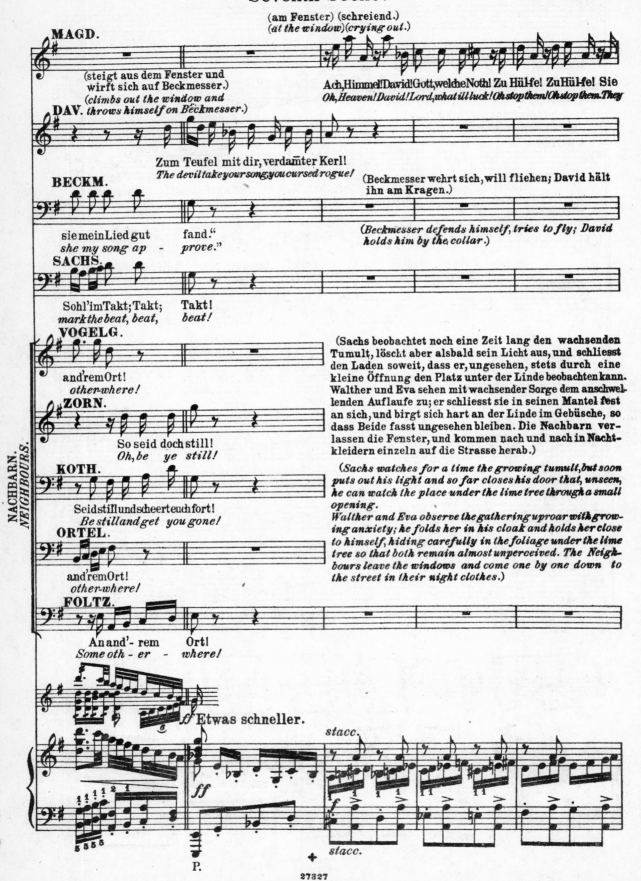

MAGD.

(am Fenster) (schreiend.)
(at the window)(crying out.)

(steigt aus dem Fenster und wirft sich auf Beckmesser.)
(climbs out the window and throws himself on Beckmesser.)

Ach, Himmel! David! Gott, welche Noth! Zu Hül-fe! Zu Hül-fe! Sie
Oh, Heaven! David! Lord, what ill luck! Oh stop them! Oh stop them. They

DAV.

Zum Teufel mit dir, verdammter Kerl!
The devil take your song you cursed rogue!

(Beckmesser wehrt sich, will fliehen; David hält ihn am Kragen.)

BECKM.

sie mein Lied gut fand."
she my song ap - prove."

(Beckmesser defends himself, tries to fly; David holds him by the collar.)

SACHS.

Sohl' im Takt; Takt; Takt!
mark the beat, beat, beat!

VOGELG.

and'rem Ort!
other-where!

ZORN.

So seid doch still!
Oh, be ye still!

(Sachs beobachtet noch eine Zeit lang den wachsenden Tumult, löscht aber alsbald sein Licht aus, und schliesst den Laden soweit, dass er, ungesehen, stets durch eine kleine Öffnung den Platz unter der Linde beobachten kann. Walther und Eva sehen mit wachsender Sorge dem anschwellenden Auflaufe zu; er schliesst sie in seinen Mantel fest an sich, und birgt sich hart an der Linde im Gebüsche, so dass Beide fasst ungesehen bleiben. Die Nachbarn verlassen die Fenster, und kommen nach und nach in Nachtkleidern einzeln auf die Strasse herab.)

(Sachs watches for a time the growing tumult, but soon puts out his light and so far closes his door that, unseen, he can watch the place under the lime tree through a small opening.
Walther and Eva observe the gathering uproar with growing anxiety; he folds her in his cloak and holds her close to himself, hiding carefully in the foliage under the lime tree so that both remain almost unperceived. The Neighbours leave the windows and come one by one down to the street in their night clothes.)

KOTH.

Seid still und scheert euch fort!
Be still and get you gone!

ORTEL.

and'rem Ort!
other-where!

NACHBARN.
NEIGHBOURS.

FOLTZ.

An and'- rem Ort!
Some oth - er - where!

ff Etwas schneller.

stacc.

ff

P.

stacc.

322

330

27327

NACHBARINNEN. / WOMEN.

2.
Ze- -ter!
Was- ser her, und
Wa- ter here, and

3.
fi- -re!
Auf, schafft nur Was- ser her! Schafft Was- ser her, und
Up, bring ye wa- ter here! Bring wa- ter here, and

4.
Ze- -ter!
fi- -re!

LEHRBUBEN. / PRENTICES.

ALT.
Kei- ner wei- che! Hal- tet selbst Ge- sel- len mu- thig Stand!
Ne- ver wa- ver! Hold your own though journey- men should come!

TENOR.
mehr!
all!
Nun hal- tet selbst Ge- sel- len mu- thig Stand! Wer wich', 'swär'
Now hold your own though journey- men should come! If you give

POGN.
Um Gott! E- va! Schliess zu! Ich seh', ob unt' im Hau- se
How now? E- va! Come in! I'll see be- low if all is

MSTR. u. NACHB. / MSTRS. & NBRS. GES. u. NACHB. / JOUR. & NBRS.

TENOR.
dran!
live!
Jetzt
'Tis

BASS.
Zünf- te her- aus!
Guilds, come ye on!

Je- der heim!
once go home!

P.
Ob. Cl. Vl.

SACHS.(die halb ohnmächtige Eva die Treppe hinaufstossend.)
(*pushing the almost fainting Eva up the steps.*)

(Pogner empfängt Eva,und zieht sie am Arm
in das Haus.Sachs,mit dem Knieriemen David eines überhauend,und mit einemFusstritt
ihn voran in den Laden stossend,zieht Walther,den er mit der andern Hand fest gefasst
hält,gewaltsam schnell ebenfalls mit sich
hinein,und schliesst sogleich fest hinter sich
zu.Beckmesser,durch Sachs von David be-
freit,sucht sich,jämmerlich zerschlagen,
eilig durch die Menge zu flüchten.)
(*Pogner receives Eva,and pulls her by the
arm into the house. Sachs giving David a
stroke with his stirrup and, sending him
into the shop by a kick, draws Walther, whom
he has seized with his other hand, quickly
and forcibly with him into the house which
he immediately closes behind him. Beckmesser, freed from David by Sachs, woe-
fully battered, hastily tries to escape through
the crowd.*)

In's Haus, Jungfer Le‑ne!
Go in, Mistress Le‑ne!

NACHTW.

Als die Strasse und Gasse leer geworden,und alle Häuser ge-
When the street and alley are empty and all the houses are
Allmählich ruhiger im
Zeitmass.

27327

schlossen sind, betritt der Nachtwächter im Vordergrunde rechts die Bühne, reibt sich die Augen, sieht
closed, the night-warder enters in front R, rubs his eyes, looks around in surprise, shakes his head

più dim.

sich verwundert um, schüttelt den Kopf, und stimmt mit leise bebender Stimme den Ruf an.)
and sings his verse with a tremulous voice.)

NACHTWÄCHTER.

Hört,   ihr Leut', und lasst euch sa - gen,   die Glock' hat
Hear,   all folk, the war-der's dit - ty;   e - le - ven

pp

el - - fe ge - schla-gen: be - wahrt euch vor Ge-spenstern und
strikes_____ in our ci - ty: de-fend yourselves from spectre and

immer mehr abnehmend.

Spuck,   dass kein bö - ser Geist eu'r Seel' be - ruck'!
sprite,   that no e - vil imp your souls af - fright!

NACHTW.

(auf dem Horn.)
(on the horn.)

(Der
(The

Lobet Gott, den Herrn!
Praiseye God the Lord!

Sehr ruhig im Zeitmass.

Vollmond tritt hervor, und scheint hell in die Gasse hinein; der Nachtwächter schreitet langsam
full moon comes out, and shines brightly into the alley, down which the Night-warder slowly
staccatissimo

dieselbe hinab.)
walks.)

(Als hier der Nachtwächter um die Ecke biegt, fällt der Vorhang schnell, genau mit dem letzten Takte.)
(As the Night-warder turns the corner, the curtain falls quickly exactly with the last chord.)

Dritter Aufzug.
Third Act.

Erste Scene.

In Sachsens Werkstatt. *(Kurzer Raum.)* Im Hintergrunde die halbgeöffnete Ladenthüre, nach der Strasse führend. Rechts zur Seite eine Kammerthüre. Links das nach der Gasse gehende Fenster, mit Blumenstöcken davor, zur Seite ein Werktisch. Sachs sitzt auf einem grossen Lehnstuhle an diesem Fenster, durch welches die Morgensonne hell auf ihn hereinscheint; er hat vor sich auf dem Schoosse einen grossen Folianten, und ist im Lesen vertieft.

First Scene.

In Sachs's workshop (Front scene.) At back the half open door leading to street. On the right side a chamber door. On the left a window looking on the alley, with flowers before it; on the same side a work bench. Sachs sits in a large arm chair at this window, through which the morning sun shines brightly upon him: he has a large folio on his lap and is arsorbed in reading it.

(David zeigt sich von der Strasse kommend unter der Ladenthüre; er lugt herein und da er Sachs gewahrt, fährt er zurück.)
(David is seen coming from the street. He peeps in and on seeing Sachs starts back.)

(Er versichert sich aber, dass Sachs ihn nicht bemerkt, schlüpft herein, stellt seinen mitgebrachten Korb auf den hinteren Werktisch beim Laden, und untersucht seinen Inhalt; er holt Blumen
(He is rearsured as Sachs does not see him and slips in, places a basket he has brought on the work bench at back by the door, and examines its contents; he takes out flowers and

und Bänder hervor, kramt sie auf dem Tische aus, und findet endlich auf dem Grunde eine Wurst und einen
ribbons, lays them out on the table and at last finds at the bottom a sausage and a cake; he prepares to

Kuchen; er lässt sich an, diese zu verzehren, als Sachs, der ihn fortwährend nicht beachtet, mit starkem Geräusch eines der grossen Blätter des Folianten umwendet.)
eat thee when Sachs who has not taken notic of him, noisily turns over a leaf of the folio.)

DAVID (fährt zusammen, verbirgt das Essen, und wendet sich zurück.)
(starts, hides the food and turns round.)

Gleich, Meister! Hier!
Yes, Master! here!

Die
The

Schuh' sind ab-ge-ge-ben in Herrn Beckmesser's Quar-tier.
shoes were taken ear-ly to Mas-ter Beckmesser's house.

Mir war's, als
Methought just

rieft ihr mich e-ben?
now that you called me?

(bei Seite)
(aside)

Er thut,
To-day

als säh' er mich
he seems not to

(Er nähert sich, sehr demüthig, langsam Sachs.)
(He approaches Sachs very humbly and slowly.

nicht? Da ist er bös', wenn er nicht spricht!
see! He does not speak: then he is cross!

Immer zurück-

DAVID.

Ach Mei - ster! Wollt mir ver-zeih'n; kann ein Lehr-bub' vollkommen
Ah Mas - ter! Will you for-give? *did a faultless prentice e'er*

haltend im Zeitmass.

sein?
live?

Kennt et ihr die Le-ne, wie
It you knew but Le-ne as

Sehr gemächlich.

ich, dann ver-gäb't ihr mir si-cher-lich. Sie ist so
I, then your par-don you'd not de - ny. *She is so*

gut, so sanft für mich, und blickt mich oft an so in - ner - lich.
good, so sweet to me, and looks at me oft so ten-der - ly.

DAVID.

Wenn ihr mich schlagt, streichelt sie mich, und lä-chelt da-bei hold - se-lig-
When you are harsh, then she is kind; her smiles will drive all care from my

lich; muss ich ca - ri - ren, füt-tert sie mich, und ist in Al-lem gar lie - be-
mind; when I am fast-ing, food she will bring, and she is lovely in ev'-ry

lich! Nur gestern, weil der Jun - ker ver - sungen, hab' ich den Korb ihr nicht ab ge-rungen. Das
thing! But last night, when she learned the knight's failure, nought would she let me take from her basket. That

schmerzte mich: Und da ich fand, dass Nacht's Einer vor dem Fenster stand, und sang zu ihr,
hurt me sore: and when I found that late, one before her window stood, and sang to her,
Etwas schneller werdend.
Belebter

DAVID.
Tag; da putzt sich je - der so schön er mag.
day, and each one decks him as best he may.

(immer leise, wie für sich.)
(still softly, as if to himself.)

SACHS.
Wär' heut' Hochzeitsfest?
Is it wed-ding day?

Ja, käm's erst so weit, dass Da-vid die Le-ne freit!
Aye, would that it were! that I might wed Le-ne fair!

(immer wie zuvor.)
(as before.)

's war
Thy

sempre stacc.

piùp

(Pol-ter-abend? Da krieg' ich's wohl noch?) Verzeiht das Meister ich bitt, ver-
(Wedding eve! Then, now for the fight?) Forgive that, Master, forget, I

Pol-ter-abend, dünkt mich doch?
wedding eve, then, was last night?

gesst! Wir feiern ja heut' Johan - nis-fest.
pray! The feast of St John we keep to-day.

(Hört er heut'
(Deaf must he

Jo-hannisfest.
Mid-summer day.

poco cresc. -

dim. -

piùp

27327

DAVID.

Kuchen!
spy it.

Möchtet ihr nicht auch die Wurst ver-su-chen?
Here, too, a sausage, would you but try it?

poco rallent.

Mässiger.

SACHS (immer ruhig ohne seine Stellung zu verändern.)
(still quietly, without changing his position.)

Schön' Dank, mein Jung'!
Good thanks, my boy!

Behalt's für dich. Doch heut' auf die Wie - se be-glei-test du
I leave it thee. But out to the mea-dow shalt thou go with

più p

mich; mit Blumen und Bän-dern putz dich fein: sollst mein statt - li-cher He - rold sein!
me. With flowers and favours make thee gay: thou my he - rald shalt be to-day!

dolce

p stacc.

DAVID.

Sollt' ich nicht lie - ber Braut-führer sein?
Might I not be your grooms man beside?

scherzando

p

zusammen und geht in die Kammer ab.)
gether and goes into the chamber.)

(Sachs, immer noch den Folianten auf dem Schoose, lehnt sich, mit untergestütztem Arm, sinnend darauf:
(Sachs, still with the folio on his lap, leans with his arms resting upon it; his talk with David does not

es scheint, dass ihn das Gespräch mit David gar nicht aus seinem Nachdenken gestört hat.)
seem to have disturbed his meditation.)

SACHS.

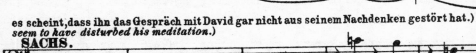

Wahn! Wahn!   Ue - ber-all
Craze! Craze!   *Ev' - ry-where*
(Posaune)

sehr weich

Wahn! Wo-hin ich for-schend blick' in Stadt-und Welt-chro - nick, den Grundmir auf - zu-
craze! In vain my looks I cast o'er pre-sentthings and past, the rea - son e - ver

Streng im Zeitmass.

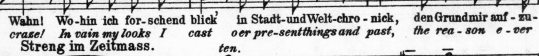

fin-den, wa-rumgar bis aufs Blut die Leut'sich quä-len und schin-den in un-nütz tol - ler
seeking, why men so fiercely fight; each one his ma - lice wreaking in aimless frenzied

SACHS.

Wuth? / spite! / ausdrucksvoll. Hat keiner Lohn noch Dank da-von: in Flucht ge-schla - gen wähnt er zu ja - gen; / He wins no wage for all his woe: and flee-ing dreams he chases his foe: his

hört nicht sein ei - gen Schmerzgekreisch, wenn er sich wühlt in's eig'ne Fleisch, wähnt / out-cry of pain he doth not hear, when he him-self his flesh doth tear, ex -

Lust sich zu er - zei-gen! Wer gibt den Na-men an? 'sist halt der al - te / ult-ing in his anguish! Ah, who shall tell its name? the craze is still the

(kräftig.) (loud.)

Wahn, ohn' den nichts mag ge-schehen, 's mag ge-hen o - der ste-hen! Steht's wo im / same: nought happens here with-out it, howe'er we go a-bout it. Stayed in its

27327

SACHS.

Lauf, er schläft nur neu - e·Kraft sich an: gleich wacht er auf, dann
course, in sleep re-turns its strength a - gain: and with new force it

schaut, wer ihn be-mei - stern kann!
wakes— ah, who can hold it then!
Etwas beschleunigend.

Ruhig wie vorher.

Wie friedsam treu - er
With peace-ful ways con-
stacc.

Sit - ten, ge - trost in That und Werk, liegt nicht in Deutschlands
tented, and help-ful work in hand, my Nür - em - burg lies

u.s.w.

SACHS.

Mit - ten   mein lie - - - bes   Nü - - ren -
plant - ed   a - midst___   our   fa - - ther -

poco cresc.

cresc.

(Er blickt mit freudiger Begeisterung ruhig vor sich hin.)
(He gazes before him in joyful enthusiasm.)

berg!
land!

sehr breit

più cresc.

ff

sehr gehalten

Doch ei-nes A - bend's   spat,   ein   Un - glück zu ver-
But on an even-ing   late,   to   safe - guard from dis-

Etwas weniger breit.

dim.

più p

hü - ten   bei ju - gend-hei-ssen Ge - mü - then, ein Mann weiss sich nicht
as - ter,   and youth-ful pas-sion to mas - ter,   a   man, fighting with

Immer etwas belebend.

stacc.

marc.

p

poco cresc.

Bass espressivo

27327

SACHS.

Rath; ein Schuster in seinem Laden zieht an des Wahnes Faden: wie bald auf Gas-sen und
fate; a shoemaker at his leather pulls at the craze's tether: then soon his neighbours a-

Strassen fängt der da an zu ra - sen! Mann, Weib, Ge-
wa - ken, by rage and pas - sion sha - - ken! Man, wife, and

sell und Kind, fällt sich da an wie toll und blind; und
youth and child, blind - - ly fall to as though gone wild; and

will's der Wahn ge-seg-nen, nun muss es Prü - gel reg-nen, mit Hieben, Stoss' und
mad - ness brings its blessing, of strife and blows un-ceasing, re-peating, aye, the

Immer lebhafter.
Noch mehr belebend.

27327

Dreschen den Wu - thesbrand zu löschen. Gott weiss, wie das ge-
story, to quell the ra - ging fury. God knows how that be-

schah? Sehr mässig.
fel!

Ein Ko - bold half wohl da: ein
A ko - bold wove the spell. In

Glühwurm fand sein Weibchen nicht;
vain his mate a glow-worm sought; der
'twas

SACHS.

schau'n wir, wie Hans Sachs es macht, dass er den Wahn fein lenken kann, ein ed - ler Werk zu
see what spell Hans Sachs can weave, that the the craze may turn the way that leads to no - ble

Etwas weniger breit *(gemächlich)*

drucksvoll

p dolce

thun: denn lässt er uns nicht ruh'n, selbst hier in Nü-ren-berg, so
works: and if this craze yet lurks e'en here in this our town, then

marc.

p stacc.

dolce

stacc.

sei's um sol - - che Werk', die sel - ten vor ge - mei - nen
let its worth___ be shown! For work hath ne-ver vir - tue

poco cresc. - - - -

Din - gen, und nie___ ohn' ein'gen Wahn_____
in it, un - less___ some help from craze

p

cresc. -

mf dim.

p

dolce

poco cresc. -

27327

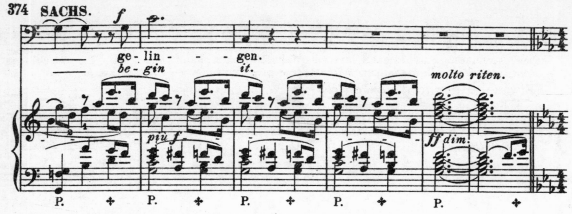

ge - lin - - gen.
be - gin - it.

Zweite Scene.
Second Scene.

(Walther tritt unter der Kammerthüre ein. Er bleibt einen Augenblick dort stehn, und blickt auf Sachs Dieser wendet sich und lässt den Folianten auf den Boden gleiten.)

(Walther enters by the chamber door. He pauses there a moment and looks at Sachs, who turns and lets the book slide to the floor.)

SACHS.

a tempo.

Ziemlich bewegt. Grüss'Gott, mein Junker!
Sir knight, I greet you!

WALTH.

(sehr ruhig)
(very quietly)

Ein we-nig, a-ber
A lit-tle, but my

Ruh-tet ihr noch! Ihr wach-tet lang, nun schlieft ihr doch?
Lay you till now? Thought late to bed, you slept, I trow?

merk'. Glaubt mir, des Men-schen wahr-ster Wahn wird ihm im Trau - me auf - ge-
lurk. Be-lieve! our deep-est wis - dom here is oft in dreams to us made

than: all' Dichtkunst und Po-e - te - rei _____ ist nichts,
clear. All po-ems that the world has known _____ are nought

als Wahr - traum-deu-te - rei. Was gilt's, es gab der Traum euch
but truths___ our dreams have shown. Perchance your dream may shew the

ein, wie heut' ihr sol-let Mei - - ster sein?
way to win the Master's prize to - day!

selbst mit euch fort-ge-laufen! Drum bitt' ich, lasst den Groll jetzt ruh'n! Ihr habt's mit
self as your guide had given! So, pray you, let your an-ger go: *you have with*

Eh - renmännern zu thun; die ir - ren sich und sind bequem, dass man auf ih - re
men of hon-our to do: mistakes they make, and each w'd find *in o-ther men the*

Wei - se sie nähm': Wer Preise er - kennt, und Prei - se stellt, der will am
thoughts of his mind: *and fair 'tis that they who grant a prize should ask what*

End' auch, dass man ihm ge - fällt. Eu'r Lied, das hat ih - nen bang ge -
seemeth goodly in their eyes. *Your song* *has filled them with dark dis-*

SACHS.

macht; und das mit Recht: denn wohl be- dacht, mit solchem Dicht' und Lie-bes-
may; and with good cause, for, truth to say, a song so full of po-et's

feu-er verführt man wohl Töchter zum A-ben - teu-er; doch für lieb-se-li-gen
passion may kin-dle our maidens in e-vil fashion; but if song calm wedded
espress.

WALTH.
(lächelnd)
(smiling)

Die kenn' ich nun auch seit die-ser
And those, too, I know since yester-

E-he-stand man and're Wort' und Wei-sen fand.
life shall speed, then other words and tunes we need.

Nacht: es hat viel Lärm auf der Gas - se ge-macht. (lachend)
night; if in the al - ley I heard them a-right. (laughing)

Ja, ja! Schon gut! Den
Aye, aye! 'Tis true! My

Fl.
Ob.

27327

380

SACHS.

Freund, in hol - der Ju - gendzeit, wenn uns von mächt'gen Trie-ben zum
friend, when youth's de - sires compel, and 'twards the goal of lov-ing the

p

sempre u.c.

cresc.

P.

sel'gen ersten Lie - ben die Brust sich schwellet hoch und weit, ein
soul is surely mov-ing, when hearts with passion beat and swell, the

f

p

poco cresc.

P.

schö - nes Lied _____ zu sin - gen mocht' vielen da ge - lin - gen: der Lenz,
boon of song _____ by Hea-ven to many then is giv - en: 'tis spring

espress.

f

dim.

P.

der sang für sie. Kam
that sings, not they. Through

p

cresc.

f

p

P.

27327

SACHS.

Sommer, Herbst und Win-ter-zeit, viel Noth und Sorg' im Leben, manch'
summer, fall and winter's spell, when life hath brought its burden, with

eh-lich Glück daneben: Kindtauf', Geschäfte, Zwist und Streit: denen's
marriage joy as guerdon: children, misfortune, strife as well: they to

dann noch _____ will ge - lin - gen ein schö - nes Lied zu
whom then _____ still by Hea - ven the grace of song is

sin - gen, seht: _____ Mei - - ster nennt man
giv - en, as _____ Mas - - ters live for

WALTH.

(Zart und begeistert anschwellend)
(*Tenderly and fervently, cresc.*)

SACHS.

Ich lieb'
I love

die!
aye!

Trp.
Pos.

ausdrucksvoll

ein Weib, und will es frei'n, mein
a maid and fain would prove, in

dau-ernd Eh'-ge-mahl zu sein.
last-ing wed-lock, all my love.

Die Mei-ster-re-geln
Then let the Master-

lernt bei Zei-ten, dass sie ge-treu---lich euch ge-
rules now speed you, that they may e---ver tru-ly

27327

lei - ten, und hel-fenwohl bewah - ren,was in den Ju - gend Jah - ren,mit
lead you, *and help to keep untaint-ed whatspring and youth have planted a -*

hol - dem Trie - be Lenz und Lie - be euch un-be-
midst youth's plea - sures; so the trea - sures,deep in the

(zart)(*tenderly*)

wusst in's Herz ge-legt, dass ihr das un - ver-lo - ren
heart in se - cret laid, throughmight of song shall ne - ver

WALTH.

Steh'n sie nun in so ho-hem
Tell me, then, if so high they

hegt!
fade!

SACHS.

ihr sie mir neu er - klä - ren.
you to our rules new mean - ing.

Seht, hier ist Tinte,
Pen, ink and paper

Feder, Papier:
ready you see:

p dolce

p dolce

P.

P.

WALTH.

Wie ich's be - gänne wüsst' ich kaum.
I know not how to start a - right.

ich schreib's euch auf, dic - tirt ihr mir!
I'll write the words you sing to me!

Er-
Think

poco cresc.

p

P.

P.

P.

P.

Durch eu'rer Re - geln gu - te Lehr'
Through all the rules that you have taught,

ist mir's als ob ver-
me seems the dream has

zählt mir euren Mor - gentraum.
on - ly of your dream this night.

p

p dolce

P.

P.

P.

P.

wischt er wär'.
come to nought.

Grad' nehmt die Dichtkunst jetzt zur Hand:
The po - et's art, then, try betimes;

Man - cher durch sie ———— das Verlor -
words that are lost ———— oft are found

cresc.

P.

27327

P.

P.

WALTH.

SACHS.

So wär's nicht Traum, doch Dich-te-
Then'twere no dream, but po - et's

- ne fand.
in rhymes.

rei?
art.

Sind Freun - - de beid', steh'n gern sich bei.
Good friends are they, ne'er far a - part.

Wie
But

fang' ich nach der Regel an?
how by rules shall I be - gin?

Ihr stellt sie selbst, und folgt ihr dann.
First make your rules, and keep them then.

Gedenkt des schönen
Think on-ly on your

Traum's am Mor - gen;
vi - sion's beau - ty:

für's And're lasst Hans Sachs nur sorgen.
to guide you well shall be my du-ty.

27327

WALTH.

SACHS.

Wa-rum ganz gleich?
Wherefore a - like?

fol-gen soll.
now succeed.

Damit man seh', ihr wähltet euch gleich ein Weib zur
To make it plain to all men that you to wed are

p

Eh'.
fain.

(anschwellend)
(cresc.)

p

"Won-nig ent - ra-gend dem se - li - gen Raum, bot gold'ner
"High o'er the gar-den a tree then did rise; the gold-en

pp   dolce

cresc. -

f

Frucht heilsaft'ge Wucht mit hol-dem Pran-gen dem Ver - lan-gen, an duft'-ger Zwei-ge
store its branches bore so richly thronging, woke my longing, when, sparkling there, my

f   dim. -   -   p

P.   ✦   P.   ✦   P.   ✦

Saum, herr-lich ein Baum."
eyes looked on the prize."

Ihr schlosset nicht im glei-chen
You end-ed in an - o - ther

cresc.   f   p

P.   ✦   P.   ✦   27327

SACHS.

Ton: das macht den Mei-stern Pein; doch nimmt Hans Sachs die Lehr' da-von, im
key: that Mas-ters blame, you know; but I, Hans Sachs, your mean-ing see; in

p

WALTH.

Was soll nun
What meaneth

Lenz wohl müss' es so sein. Nun stellt mir ei - nen „Ab - ge-sang!"
spring it needs must be so. An "Af - tersong" now sing as well.

cresc.

p

der?
that?

poco rall.

Ob euch ge - lang, ein rech - tes Paar zu fin - den, das
The child will tell, if true and fit - ly ma - ted, the

Etwas zurückgehalten.

p

p

poco rall.

a tempo.

poco rall.

zeigt sich an den Kin - den; den Stol-len ähn-lich, doch nicht gleich, an eig'-nen
pair by you cre - a - ted; though like the stanzas; yet its own and new must

a tempo.

a tempo. rall.

p

SACHS (gerührt.)
(moved.)

Das nenn' ich mir ei-nen Ab-gesang! Seht wie der gan-ze Bar gelang! Nur mit der Me-lo-
In sooth, I call that an Af-tersong! See how the verse now flows along! But with the me-lo-

dei seid ihr ein we-nig frei: doch sag' ich nicht dass das ein Feh-ler sei;
dy are you a lit-tle free. Yet say I not that that's a fault with me:

nur ist's nicht leicht zu be-hal-ten, und das är-gert uns'-re Al-ten.
but for the ear 'tis perplexing, and to old men that is vex-ing.

Jetzt richtet mir noch ei-nen zwei-ten Bar, damit man merk' welch' der er-ste war. Auch
A se-cond verse must you now compose, to fix in mind how the first one goes. And

WALTH.

hell, wie strahl - ten die Ster - ne da schön! Zu Tanz und
bright, new gath - er - ing stars___ on me beam, as, gai - ly

Rei - gen in Laub und Zwei - gen, der gold'nen sam-meln sich
danc - ing, through branch - es glanc - ing, their golden lus - tre they

mehr, statt Frucht ein Ster-nen - heer im Lor - - - - - - beer -
shed; not fruit but stars o'er spread the lau - - - - - - - rel___

baum."
tree."

SACHS.

(sehr gerührt.)
(much moved.)

Freund,___ euer Traumbild wies euch
Friend,___ your vi - sion told you

molto riten. *sehr ausdrucksvoll*
Allmählich wieder zurückgehend

27327

SACHS.

Wort ____ am rechten Ort! ____ Drum bitt' ich, merkt mir wohl die Weise: gar
deed ____ let fortune speed! ____ I pray you, well the tune remember, right

lieb-lich drinn sich's dich-ten lässt. Und singt ihr sie im weit' - ren
well it suits with such a theme, and, when before the folk you

WALTH.

Was habt ihr vor?
What would you do?

Krei - se, so hal-tet mir auch das Traumbild fest.
sing it, hold fast in your mind that morning dream.

Eur treu - er Knecht fand sich mit Sack und Tasch' zu recht: die Klei -
Your trus - ty squire, bearing your packs, with that at - tire wherein ____

27327

- der, drinn am Hoch-zeits-fest da-heim___ ihr woll-tet
to grace your wed-ding-feast at-home___ youmeant to

prangen,dieliesser her zu mir ge-lan-gen ein Täub-chen
prink you,hasfoundhisway to me,howthinkyou? Some bird,___ sure,

zeigt ihmwohl das Nest, da-rin sein Jun-ker träumt.___ Drumfolgtmirjetztin's
must have shewnthe nest where-in his mas-ter dreams.___ Thenwithme to your

Kämmerlein: mit Klei-den, wohl ge-säumt, sol-len bei-de wir ge-
chamber go; for rai-ment gay be-seems such a task as lies be-

SACHS.

zie - - - ret sein, wenn's Statt - li - ches zu
fore us now; by dar - - ing deeds to

poco cresc.

Vl.

mf sempre più cresc.

P.

wa - - gen gilt. Drum
reach our ends. So

stacc.

stacc.

P. P. P.

kommt, seid ihr gleich mir ge - sinnt.
come, if you and I are friends.

Vl. Vl. Tr.
Pos.
ff
Etwas breit.

ff
marc.

P. P. P.

27327

402

(Walther schlägt in Sachsen's Hand ein, so geleitet ihn dieser ruhig festen
Schrittes zur Kammer, deren Thüre er ihm ehrerbietig öffnet, und dann ihm folgt.)
(Walther grasps Sachs's hand, who leads him with a quiet, firm step to the
chamber door, opening it for him respectfully and then following him.)

(Man gewahrt Beckmesser, welcher draussen vor dem Laden erscheint, in grosser Aufgeregtheit
(Beckmesser appears outside the shop window, looking in, in great perturbation. Finding the shop

hereinlugt, und da er die Werkstatt leer findet, hastig hereintritt.)
empty he enters hastily.)

27827

Dritte Scene.
Third Scene.

BECKM. (Er ist sehr aufgeputzt, aber in sehr leidendem Zustande.)
(He is dressed very richly, but seems very miserable.)
(Er blickt sich erst unter der Thüre nochmals genau in der Werkstatt um.)
(He peeps again carefully round the shop from the doorway.)

Sehr mässig.

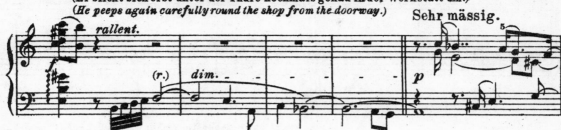

(Dann hinkt er vorwärts, zuckt aber zusammen, und streicht sich den Rücken.)
(He then limps forwards, winces in pain
and rubs his back.)

(Er macht wieder einige Schritte, knickt aber
mit den Knien, und streicht nun diese.)
(After a few more steps forward his knees give
way. He rubs them.)

(Er setzt sich auf den Schusterschemel, fährt aber
schnell schmerzhaft wieder auf.)
(He sits on the cobbler's stool, but starts up again
in pain.)

(Er betrachtet sich den
(He contemplates the stool,
Etwas lebhaft und im-

Schemel und geräth dabei in immer aufgeregteres Nachsinnen.)
and his thoughts appear to become increasingly agitated.)
mer mehr belebend.

(Er wird von den verdriesslichsten Erinnerungen und Vorstellungen gepeinigt; immer unruhiger be-
(He is distressed by the most grievous memories and fancies; getting ever more uneasy, he begins

ginnt er sich den Schweiss von der Stirne zu wischen.)
to wipe the perspiration from his brow.)

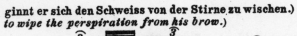

(Er hinkt immer lebhafter umher und starrt dabei vor sich hin.)
(He limps round more and more restlessly, staring before him.)

sempre cresc.

(Als ob er
(As if pursued

stacc.

sf

più f

von allen Seiten verfolgt wäre, taumelt er fliehend hin und her.)
from all sides, he stumbles hither and thither as in flight.)

Immer schneller.

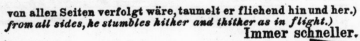

p stacc. *cresc.*

(Wie um nicht umzusinken hält er sich an dem Werktisch, zu dem
er hingeschwankt war, an, und starrt vor sich hin.)
*(As though to save himself from falling he holds on to the table, to
which he has tottered, and stares before him.)*

Sehr schnell.

stacc.

ff

(Matt und verzweiflungsvoll sieht
(*Weak and in despair he looks around.*

Sehr mässig.

sein Blick fällt endlich durch das
At length his glance fall on Pog-

er um sich:—

Fenster auf Pogner's Haus; er hinkt mühsam an dasselbe heran und nach dem gegenüberliegenden Fen-
ner's house through the window to which he limps with difficulty, and looking at the opposite window

ster ausspähend, versucht er sich in die Brust zu werfen, als ihm sogleich Ritter Walther einfällt.)
tries to assume a bold manner as he thinks of Walther.)

(Ärgerliche Gedanken entstehen dadurch, gegen die er mit schmei-
chelndem Selbstgefühle anzukämpfen sucht.)
(*Angry thoughts arise in consequense which he tries to fight down
by an assumption of selfconfidence.*)

(Die Eifersucht übermannt ihn; er schlägt sich vor den Kopf.)
(Jealonsy overcomes him. He strikes his forehead.)

(Er glaubt die Verhöhnung der Weiber und Buben auf der Gasse zu
(He fancies that he hears again the mocking of the women and boys

Immer schneller.   **Sehr schnell.**

vernehmen, wendet sich wüthend ab, und schmeisst das Fenster zu.)
in the alley; turns away in a rage and slams the window to.)

(Sehr verstört wendet er sich mechanisch wieder dem Werktische zu, indem er
(Much disturbed he turns mechanically again to the work-table which he con-

Sehr mässig (wie zuvor.)

vor sich hinbrütend, nach einer neuen Weise zu suchen scheint.)
templates as he appears to be seeking a new tune.)

BECKM.

SACHS.

Schon gut der Witz', und ge-nug der Streich! Glaubt mir, Freund Sachs:
Enough of jests! Though your wit is keen, trust me, friend Sachs,

weich.___
thin.
stacc.

jetzt kenn' ich euch! Der Spass von die - ser Nacht, der wird euch noch ge-
your guile is seen! Your trick of yes - ter - day you will not soon for-

dacht. Dass ich euch nur nicht im We - ge sei,
get. So that I should not ob - struct your way,

schuft ihr gar Auf-ruhr und Meute - rei!
uproar and fighting a stir you set!

'swar Pol - ter - abend, lasst euch te-
'Twas wed - ding eve, let me re-

BECKM.

poco rit.   *a tempo*

Darum! Darum! Wär'ich so dumm? Mit Schreien und mit Klo - pfen wollt
And so! *and so!* *ah now I know! with voice and ham-mer ring - ing, you*

er mein Lied zu - sto - pfen, dass nicht dem Kind werd' kund wie auch ein And'rer be-stund.
sought to drown my sing - ing, lest she should un-der-stand, an-o - ther stood there at hand.

Ja, ja! haha! Hab' ich dich da? Aus seiner Schuster-stu - ben hetzt'
Aye, aye! Ho, ho! 'tis e - ven so? Di - rected by your cun - ning, the

end-lich er den Bu - ben mit Knüppeln auf mich her, dass mei-ner los er wär'!
boys in packs came run-ning, with cudgels for the fray, to drive me from your way!

Au, au! Au, au! Wohl grün und blau, zum Spott der al - ler - lieb - sten
And now through you, I'm black and blue, and shamed be-fore the maid - en

Frau, zer-schlagen und zer - prü-gelt, dass kein Schneider mich auf-
too! With tooth and nail they tore me: ne'er a tai - lor could re-

bü-gelt! Gar auf mein Le - ben war's an-ge-ge - ben!
store me! Suspicions fill me, they meant to kill me.

Doch kam ich noch so da-von, dass ich die That euch lohn': zieht heut' nur aus zum
Yet by luck I got a-way, that I my debt might pay Go forth when all as-

Singen, merkt auf wie's mag ge - lin-gen!
semble, to-day your voice may tremble.
Bin ich ge - zwackt auch - und zer -

hackt, euch bring' ich doch si-cher aus dem Takt.
soon, for I will yet put you out of tune.

SACHS.

Gut Freund, ihr seid in ar - gem Wahn; glaubt was ihr
Good friend, your wits are o - ver - cast. Think what you
Sehr allmählich in der Schnelligkeit nachlassend.

wollt, dass ich ge-than; gebt eu're Ei-fer-sucht nur hin; zu wer -
will of what is past: be notth rough jealou-sy so blind; for woo -
Hier bereits mässige Bewegung.

418

SACHS.

dass man von euch auch nicht Üb-les denkt, behal-tet das Blatt, es sei euch ge-
men for this act-ion might call you thief! To save you from that, I give you the

cresc.

BECKM. (in freudigem Schreck aufspringend.)
(spinging up in joyful surprise.)

Herr Gott!   Ein Ge-dicht?
Good Lord!   A   song?

schenkt.
leaf.

glissando   gliss.

P.   P.

Ein Gedicht von Sachs?   Doch halt',
A   song   by   you?   Yet stay,

gliss.

P.

dass kein neuer Schad' mir erwachs'!   Ihr habt's wohl schon recht gut memo-
lest mis-hap should cross me anew!   The song you have, no doubt, got by
                                            poco riten.

più p   pp   ppp

u. c.

27827

BECKM.

deu - ten. Und seht nur, wie mir's er - geht, wie's mit mir Ärmsten
tru - ly. And look you! sad is my plight, since the ills of the

steht! Er - seh' ich doch mit Schmerzen, das Lied, das
night, with heart ach - ing and doubting, when - e'er I

Nachts ich sang, Dank eu'ren lust'gen Scherzen! es machte der Pog - nerin
think on my lay. Thanks to your foolish flouting, the maiden was filled with dis-

bang'. Wie schaff' ich mir nun zur Stel - le ein neu - es
may. How can I, with all my learning, now make a-

27327

BECKM.

wie käm's, dass nach so grosser Be-schwer' ihr's freund-lich heut' mit mir
how comes it, af-ter all that has passed, a friend I find you to-

poco riten.

più p   *pp*

mein't?
day?

SACHS.

Ich macht euch Schuh' in spä-ter Nacht: hat man je so einen Feind be-
Till late at night I made your shoes; is't so that men e-ver serve their

a tempo.   *dolce*

P. ✠ P. ✠ P. ✠ *sempre con Ped.*

Ja, ja! Recht gut! Doch Ei-nes schwört: wo und wie ihr das Lied auch hört, dass nie ihr euch
Ay, ay! 'Tis true! Yet one thing swear, that when-e-ver this song you hear, you ne-ver will

dacht?
foes?

beikommen lasst, zu sa-gen das Lied sei von euch verfasst.
bring me to shame, and, though I should win, you will make no claim.

Das schwör ich,
My promise

poco cresc.

27327

SACHS.

und gelob' es euch: nie mich zu rühmen, das Lied sei von
and my oath I give; ne'er will I claim it, so long as I

dim. - - - *più p*

poco riten.

BECKM. (sich vergnügt die Hände reibend.)
(rubbing his hands with delight.)

Was will ich mehr? Ich bin ge - bor - gen: jetzt braucht sich Beckmesser
What would I more? Ill-luck is o - ver: Beck - mes - ser now will hence-

mir.
live.

sf pp   *cresc.* -

nicht mehr zu sor - gen.
forth live in clo - ver.

Doch, Freund, ich führ's euch zu Ge - mü - the,
But, friend, now deem me not a scoff - er,

stacc.   *stacc.*

f   *p*   *f*

und rath' es euch in al - ler Gü - te: studirt mir recht das
if coun - sel good to you I of - fer: to con the song with

sempre stacc.

p

27327

SACHS.

Lied; sein Vor - trag ist nicht leicht; ob euch die
heed; not ea - sy 'tis to sing. The "mode" may

Wei - se ge - rieth', und ihr den Ton er - reicht.
fail at your need, the "tone" may false - ly ring.

BECKM.

Freund Sachs, ihr seid ein gu-ter Po - et; doch was Ton und Wei-se be-trifft, gesteht, da
Friend Sachs, as po - et, first is your place, but when "tones" and "modes" are in hand, confess, that

thut mir's Kei - ner vor. Drum spitzt nur fein das Ohr, und:
I need have no fear. Then o - pen well your ear, and:

„Beckmesser! Keiner besser!" Darauf macht euch ge-fasst, wenn ihr mich ruhig singen
"Beckmesser! Tone-professor!" *And all your doubt will cease,* *if you let me but sing in*

poco riten..

lasst. Doch nun memo-ri-ren, schnell nach Haus: oh-ne Zeit zu ver-
peace. *But now I must learn it well by heart:* *that no time may be*

a tempo (lebhaft.)

lie - ren richt' ich das aus. Hans Sachs, mein Theu-rer, ich
wast - ed, I must de - part. *Hans Sachs, my comrade, your*

hab' euch ver - kannt; durch den A - ben-teu - rer war ich ver-
heart I mis - read; *by the knight of Stolz - ing I was mis-*

BECKM.

(sehr zutraulich.)
(very confidentially.)

rannt: so Ei-ner fehlte uns blos! Den wurden wir Meister doch
led: we well can spare such as he! We Masters from him now are

poco riten.

dim. p cresc. f dim.

los!__ Doch mein Be-sinnen läuft mir von hin-nen!
free. But all my senses scat-ter and leave me!

a tempo.

p stacc. p cresc. p cresc._

Bin ich ver-wirrt, und ganz verirrt? Die Sil-ben, die
Are my wits dazed and all astray? The stanzas, the

f p stacc.

Reime, die Worte, die Verse! Ich kleb' wie am Leime, und brennt doch die
accents, the measure, the verses! I stay here and chatter, with feet all on

cresc._ f. p cresc._

Fer-se. / fire. A - de! Ichmussfort: an·andrem Ort dank' ich euch
Fare-well! I must go: wemeet a - gain. Thanks in sin-

in - niglich, weil ihr so min - niglich; für euch nur stim-me ich, kauf' eu - re
cer - i - ty take for your friend-li-ness; you shall my vote command, all of your

Wer - ke gleich, ma-che zum Mer - ker euch, doch fein mit Krei-de weich, nicht mit dem
works I'll buy, you shall our Mark - er be, but on-ly chalk we use; mark not with

Ham-merstreich! Mer-ker! Merker! Merker Hans Sachs!
hammer blows! Marker! Marker! Marker, Hans Sachs!

27327

BECKM.

Dass Nürn - berg schus-ter-lich blüh' und
That Nürn - berg e - ver may bloom and

p stacc.
cresc.

wachs'!
wax!

Vl.

u.s.f.

f stacc.

(Beckmesser nimmt tanzend von
(Beckmesser, dancing about, takes

P.

Sachs Abschied, taumelt und poltert der Ladenthüre zu; plötzlich glaubt er das Gedicht in seiner
leave of Sachs and hurries stumbling to the door; suddenly the thinks he has forgotten to pocket

più f stacc.

ff

Tasche vergessen zu haben; läuft wieder vor, sucht ängstlich auf dem Werktische, bis er es in der
the song, comes forward again and anxiously seeks it on the table, until he discovers it in his

Vl.
Br.
ff
ff

Cb. in 8va.

eigenen Hand gewahr wird: darüber scherzhaft erfreut, umarmt er Sachs nochmals, voll feurigen Dankes,
hand; delighted thereat, he again embraces Sachs, in fervent gratitude, and then rushes, limping and stum-

und stürzt dann, hinkend und strauchelnd, geräuschvoll durch die Ladenthüre ab.)
bling noisily, through the shop door.)

(Sachs sieht Beckmesser gedankenvoll lächelnd nach.)
(Sachs follows Beckmesser with his eyes, thoughtfully smiling.)

Allmählich mässiger werdend.

poco a poco dim.

SACHS.

So ganz bos - haft doch Kei - nen ich
Such rank ma - lice ne'er yet have I

fand; er hält's auf die Län - ge nicht aus:
known; ere long he will meet with his meed:

vergeudet Mancher
though many squander

oft viel Ver - stand, doch hält er auch da - mit
wits that they own, yet keep e - nough for their

Vierte Scene.

(Eva reich geschmückt,in glänzend weisser Kleidung,etwas leidend und blass, tritt zum Laden herein, und

Fourth scene.

(*Eva richly dressed in gleaming white, rather sad and pale,enters the shop and comes slowly forward.*)

SACHS.

blieb'!
be?
Grüss'Gott, mein Ev'chen! Ei, wie herrlich und
Good day, my Ev'chen! Ei, art arming thy-

Mässig.

p dolce

poco cresc.

tr

schreitet langsam vor.)

stolz du's heute meinst! Du machst wohl Alt und Jung begehrlich,
self with weapons fine, both old and young by beauty charming,

mf ausdrucksvoll.

dim.

wenn du so schön er - scheinst.
that thou so bright dost shine?

EVA.

Meister, 's ist nicht so ge - fährlich: und
Mas-ter, 'tis not so a - larming: though

p dolce

27327

EVA.

ste - he, will es geh'n; doch will ich geh'n, zwingt mich's zu
stand, it will a - way; but when I move it makes me

steh'n.
stay.

SACHS.

Hier auf den Schemel streck' den Fuss: der üblen Noth ich weh - ren
Up - on the stool here place the shoe, and I will see what I can

(Sie streckt einen Fuss auf dem Schemel
(She places one foot on the stool near

am Werktisch aus.)
the table.)

Ihr seht, zu weit!
Too broad, you see!

muss. Was ist mit dem?
do. What's wrong with that?

Kind, das ist pu - re Ei - telkeit; der Schuh ist knapp.
Child, that is nought but va - ni - ty; the shoe fits close.

Das
Yes,

436

SACHS.

mich. Du hörst nicht drauf? So sprich doch jetzt; hast mir's ja selbst in den Kopf ge-
me, Thou hear'st me not? Now speak a word; for first the plan from thy lips I

setzt! Schon gut! _ ich merk': _ „mach' dei-ne
heard. 'Tis well! I see! "Make but thy

Schuh'!" Säng' mir nur wenigstens Ei-ner da-zu! Hör-te heut' gar ein schönes
shoes!" If I could only now summon my muse! Lately a beauteous song I

Lied: wem da-zu wohl ein drit-ter Vers ge-rieth?
heard: would but some one now sing me verse the third!

WALTH. (den begeisterten Blick unverwandt auf Eva geheftet.)
(gazing in rapture on Eva.)

Weil-ten die Ster-ne im lieb-li-chen Tanz? So licht und
Lured from their dan-ces the stars glided down, and sparkled

klar im Lo-ckenhaar, vor al-len Frau-en hehr zu schauen, lag ihr mit zar-tem
fair a-bout her hair; on her at-tend-ing, beauty lending, and round her head there

Glanz ein Ster-nen-kranz! Wun-der ob
shone a star-ry crown. Won-der on

SACHS (immer fort arbeitend)
(still working)

Lausch', Kind! Das ist ein Mei-ster-lied.
Hark, child! that is a Mas-ter-song.

Wun-der nun bie-ten sich dar: zwie-fa-chen Tag ich grüssen
won-der was born on the height: ere night was gone a two-fold

WALTH.

mag; denn, gleich zwei'n Son - nen reinster Won-nen, der hehrsten Au - gen
dawn was ris-ing o'er me as be-fore me, like suns, her eyes so

Paar nahm' ich da wahr.
bright greet - ed my sight.

Huld - reich-stes
Oh, hal - lowed

SACHS (bei Seite zu Eva)
(aside to Eva)

Der-lei hörst du jetzt bei mir sin - gen.
Such songs are heard now in my dwell - ing.

Bild, dem ich zu na-hen mich er - kühnt! Den Kranz, von zwei - er Sonnen
scene, that like a spell my footsteps drew! Lit up by sun - beams richly

Strahl zugleich ge - bli - chen und er - grünt,
shed, the wreath grew pale and bloomed a - new.

27327

WALTH.

traum!
dream.

(Eva, die wie bezaubert regungslos gestanden, gesehen und gehört hat, bricht jetzt in
(*Eva, who has stood motionless as if enchanted, gazing and listening, now passion -*

Sehr lebhaft.

heftiges Weinen aus, sinkt Sachs an die Brust, und drückt ihn schluchzend an sich. Walther ist zu ihnen getre-
ately bursts into tears, sinks on Sachs's breast, and presses herself to him, sobbing. Walther has come to them;

ten; er drückt begeistert Sachs die Hand. Sachs thut sich endlich Gewalt an, reisst sich wie unmuthig los, und
he presses Sachs's hand. Sachs at length controls himself and tears himself moodily away; and so leaves Eva

SACHS.

lässt dadurch Eva unwillkürlich an Walther's Schulter sich anlehnen.)
involuntarily leaning on Walther's shoulder.)

Hat
A

man mit dem Schuh-werk nicht sei-ne Noth!⸺ Wär'
shoe-ma-ker's life is aye full of care!⸺ and

ich nicht noch Po-et ⸺⸺⸺ da-zu,
were I not a po-⸺⸺⸺-et too,

ich mach-te län-⸺⸺-ger kei-ne Schuh'!
henceforth I ne'er⸺⸺ would make a shoe!

Das ist ei-ne Müh', ein Auf-ge-bot! Zu weit dem Ei-nen, dem
No rest; e-ver culled, now here, now there! Too wide for this one, for

27327

SACHS.

An-dern zu eng';
that one too small.

von al-len Sei-ten
To all his neighbou

Lauf' und Ge-
nds-man and

dräng': da klappt's, da schlappt's, hier drückt's, da zwickt's; der
thrall. Too loose, too tight, too thick, too slight. The

Schuster soll auch Al-les wissen, flicken was nur im-mer zer-ris-sen:
cobbler must have wit un - ending, patching all the holes that need mending:

und ist er gar Po-et da-zu, da lässt man am End' ihm auch da kei-ne Ruh';
and if he be a po-et too, no rest can he find then, but toil e-ver new;

SACHS.

und ist er erst noch Wittwer gar, zum Nar - ren hält man ihn für-wahr:
should he a widow-er chance to be; *to fool him well then all a-gree:*

die jüng - sten Mäd-chen, ist Noth an Mann, be - geh-ren, er
the young-est maid-ens, when woo-ers fail, ex-pect him to

hiel-te um sie an; ver-steht er sie, ver-steht er sie nicht,
tell the lover's tale; *and if he know,* *or know not their ways,*

all eins ob ja, ob nein er spricht, am End' riecht er doch nach
all one, if yes or no he says. *They smell pitch a-bout the*

SACHS.

Pech,— und gilt für dumm; tückisch und frech.
place!— they call him dull, knavish and base.

Ei! 'sist mir nur um den Lehr-bu-ben leid; der ver-liert mir al-len Respekt: die
Ah! I am grieved for the prentice, I say: all re-spect he loses for me: for

Le - ne macht ihn schon nicht recht gescheit, dass aus Töpf' und Tellern er leckt. Wo Teu-fel er
Le - ne spoils him by night and by day, and a la-zy glutton is he. The de-vil now

EVA (indem sie Sachs zurückhält und von Neuem an sich zieht.)
(as she holds Sachs back and again draws him to her.)

O Sachs!— Mein Freund! Du
O Sachs!— My friend! My

jetzt nur wie-der steckt!
knows where he can be!

theu - - - rer Mann! Wie ich dir
on - - ly friend! All I shall

Ed - - lem loh - nen kann! Was oh - ne dei - ne
owe _____ thee till the end! What but for thy love's

Lie - be, ___ was wär' ich oh - ne dich? ob
keep - ing, ___ what were I but for thee? In

je auch Kind ich blie - be, er - weck - test du mich
child - hood's dream yet sleep - ing, hads't thou not wa - kened

EVA.

bang.
dare.

SACHS.

Mein Kind, von Tris-tan und I - sol-de kenn' ich ein trau-rig
My child, of Tris-tan and I - sol-de, a grievous tale I

Etwas mässiger.

Stück: Hans Sachs war klug und woll - te nichts von Herrn Mar-ke's Glück. 'swar
know: Hans Sachs was wise and would not en - dure king Mar-ke's woe. To

poco riten. a tempo.

Zeit, dass ich den Rechten fand, wär' sonst am End' doch hinein ge - rannt.
find the man be-fore too late, I sought, or else that had been my fate.

Sehr lebhaft

A - ha! Da streicht die Lene schon um's Haus: nur her - ein, He!
A - ha! Al - rea - dy Lene is a - bout: come you in! Ho!

(Magdalena in festlichem Staate, tritt durch die Laden-thüre herein. David, ebenfalls im Festkleid, mit Blumen und Bändern sehr reich und zierlich aufgeputzt, kommt zugleich aus der Kammer heraus.)
(*Magdalena, in festal array, enters through the shop door. David, also dressed for the festival, decked out with flowers and ribbons, comes out of the chamber at the same time.*)

SACHS.

David! Komm'st nicht her - aus? Die
David! Thou too, come out. The

Zeu - gen sind da, Ge - vat - ter zur Hand: jetzt schnell zur
wit - nes - ses here, and sponsors at hand! So, for the

(Alle blicken ihn verwun-dert an.)
(*All look at him in surprise.*)

Tau - fe! Nehmt eu'ren Stand!
christ' - ning, take now your stand!

Ein Kind ward hier ge - boren: Jetzt sei ihm ein Nam'er -
A child, new-ly cre - at-ed, with a name shall now be

Merklich langsamer.

27327

SACHS.

koren. So ist's nach Meisterweis' und Art, wenn ei-ne Mei - ster-wei - se ge-schaf-fen
mated. This is by use the Masters' right— whene'er a Mas-ter-mode has been brought to

ausdrucksvoll

ward, dass die ei-nen gu-ten Na-men trag', d'ran Je - der sie er-ken-nen
light, the strain by a goodly name they call, and so hence-forth 'tis known to

poco rall.

p

poco cresc.

mag. Vernehmt, re-spek-ta-ble Ge - sell - - schaft,
all. *Now know, worthy people, who hear me,*

marcato

was euch hier zur Stell' schafft! Ei-ne Meisterwei-se ist ge-
why I call you near me. Here a "Mastermode" was fashioned

SACHS.

lun-gen, von Junker Wal - ther ge-dich-tet und ge - sun-gen: der jungen Wei-se le-ben-der
newly: and by this knight has been sung be-fore us du-ly: he asks that we our aid now may

Va - ter lud mich und die Pog-ne - rin zu Ge - vat - - - - - -
lend him, and straight at its bap-tism here at - tend_____

- - ter.
_____ *him.*

weil wir die Wei-se wohl ver-nommen
As to his song our ears have listened,

sind wir zur Tau-fe hier-her ge - kom - men; auch dass wir zur Handlung Zeu-gen ha-ben, ruf'
we hith-er come that it may be christened. That we who have heard at - test its fitness, let

ich JungferLene undmei - nen Kna - - - ben.
David and Lene nowstand to___ wit - - - ness.

Doch da's zum Zeu-gen kein Lehr-bu - be thut, und heut auch den Spruch er ge-sun-gen
But as no prentice a wit-ness may be, and right well to - day he has sung to

gut, so mach' ich den Burschen gleich zum Ge-sell'. Knie' nie-der, David, und nimm die-se
me, a jour-ney-man I will make of him now. Kneel, David, and, on thy knees, take this

(David ist niedergekniet;
Sachs giebt ihm eine starke Ohrfeige.)
*(David has knelt;
Sachs gives him a smart box on the ear.)*

Schell'.
blow.

Steh' auf, Ge-sell', und
A - rise, the blow thou

denk' an den Streich: du merkst dir da-bei die Tau-fe zu-gleich. Fehlt sonst noch'was,
wilt not forget: the bap - tism that will fix in thy pate. If aught should lack,

uns kei - ner schilt; wer weiss, ob's nicht gar ei-ner Noth - tau - fe
what blame in - deed? Per - chance 'tis "half - bap-tism" we now may

gilt. Dass die Wei - se Kraft be - hal - te zum Le-ben, will ich nur gleich den
need. That the mode's good - luck may last on un-broken, be-fore you, let its

Na - men ihr ge - ben: Die „se - li - ge Mor - gen-traum =
name be now spok - en The mode of the "Morn - ing

SACHS.

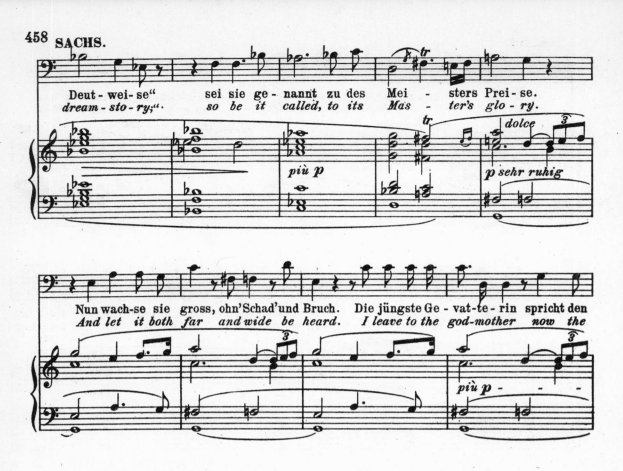

Deut - wei - se" sei sie ge - nannt zu des Mei - sters Prei - se.
dream - sto - ry;" *so be it called, to its Mas - ter's glo - ry.*

Nun wach - se sie gross, ohn' Schad' und Bruch. Die jüngste Ge - vat - te - rin spricht den
And let it both far and wide be heard. I leave to the god - mother now the

(Er tritt aus der Mitte des Halbkreises, der von den Uebrigen um ihn gebildet worden war, auf die Seite, so dass nun Eva in der Mitte zu stehen kommt.)
(He moves from the middle of the half-circle which the others have formed round him, so that Eva stands now in the middle.)

Spruch.
word.

EVA.

Se - - - lig, wie die Son - ne mei - nes Glü - ckes lacht,
Bright - ly as the sun up - on my for - tune breaks,

Langsam, doch leicht fliessend.

27327

P.

(Eva und Magdalene gehen)
(Eva and Magdalene go)

(zu Walther)
(to Walther)

SACHS.

Gleiche Bewegung (♩ = ♪)

p stacc.

Nun, Jun-ker, kommt!
Now come, Sir knight!

Habt fro-hen
Your ills are

Muth!
past.

David,
David,

Ge-sell':
lock up:

schliess'den La-den gut!
leave all safe and fast!

p   *sempre stacc.*

(Als Sachs und Walther
(As Sachs and Walther

ebenfalls auf die Strasse gehen, und David über das Schliessen der Ladenthüre sich hermacht, wird im Proscenium ein Vorhang von beiden Seiten zusammengezogen, so dass er die Scene gänzlich verschliesst.)
go together into the street and David sets himself to lock up the shop doors, a curtain is drawn from both sides in the Proscenium closing in the scene.)

un poco cresc.

Allmählich etwas belebter im

Zeitmass.

(Hörner auf dem Theater, entfernt aufgestellt und sehr stark geblasen.)
(Horns on the stage, distant and very loudly played.)

(Trompeten auf dem Theater, den Hörnern
(Trumpets on the stage, opposite the Horns.)

entgegengesetzt.)

(Trompeten auf dem Theater.)
(Trumpets on the stage.)

Fünfte Scene.

Die Vorhänge sind nach der Höhe aufgezogen worden; die Bühne ist verwandelt. Diese stellt einen freien Wiesenplan dar, im fernen Hintergrunde die Stadt Nürnberg. Die Pegnitz schlängelt sich durch den Plan; der schmale Fluss ist an den nächsten Punkten praktikabel gehalten. Bunt beflaggte Kähne setzen unablässig die ankommenden, festlich gekleideten Bürger der Zünfte, mit Frauen und Kindern, an das Ufer der Festwiese über. Eine erhöhte Bühne, mit Bänken und Sitzen darauf, ist rechts zur Seite aufgeschlagen; bereits ist sie mit den Fahnen der angekommenen Zünfte ausgeschmückt; im Verlaufe stecken die Fahnenträger der noch ankommenden Zünfte ihre Fahnen ebenfalls um die Sängerbühne auf, so dass diese schliesslich nach 3 Seiten hin ganz davon eingefasst ist. Zelte mit Getränken und Erfrischungen aller Art begrenzen im Uebrigen die Seiten des vorderen Hauptraumes.

Vor den Zelten geht es bereits lustig her: Bürger, mit Frauen, Kindern und Gesellen, sitzen und lagern daselbst. — Die Lehrbuben der Meistersinger, festlich gekleidet, mit Blumen und Bändern reich und anmuthig geschmückt, üben mit schlanken Stäben, die ebenfalls mit Blumen und Bändern geziert sind, in lustiger Weise das Amt von Herolden und Marschällen aus. Sie empfangen die am Ufer Aussteigenden, ordnen die Züge der Zünfte, und geleiten diese nach der Sängerbühne, von wo aus, nachdem der Bannerträger die Fahne aufgepflanzt, die Zunftbürger und Gesellen nach Belieben sich unter den Zelten zerstreuen. So eben, nach der Verwandlung, werden in der angegebenen Weise die Schuster am Ufer empfangen, und nach dem Vordergrund geleitet.

Fifth Scene.

The curtains have been drawn up and a new scene represents an open meadow with the town of Nuremberg in the distance. The Pegnitz, a narrow stream, practicable at its nearest part, winds across the stage. From gaily decorated boats which arrive continually at the bank, Burghers of the guilds, with women and children in festival costume, land on the meadow. A raised platform with chairs and benches on it has been erected on the right, decked with the banners of those Guilds which have already arrived. As new Guilds come on, their banner-bearers also plant their banners around the platform so as finally to close it in entirely on 3 sides. Tents with drinks and refreshments of all kinds on sides of stage.

In front of the tents there is merry making; Burghers with women and children and Journeymen sit and lie about there. Prentices of the Mastersingers, richly decked with flowers and ribbons, with slender staves similarly adorned, merrily act the parts of heralds and marshals; they receive the new arrivals on the shore, order the processions of Guilds and lead them to the singers' platform, whence, after the banner-bearers have planted the banners, the Burghers and Journeymen disperse as they please at the booths. As the curtains rise the Shoemakers are being thus received at the bank and conducted to the front.

470

DIE SCHUSTER.
THE SHOEMAKERS.

gu - te Zeit, macht' ih - nen war - me Schuh'; und
mer - ry time; well shod from toe to heel; if

gu - te Zeit, macht' ih - nen war - me Schuh'; und
mer - ry time; well shod from toe to heel; if

gu - te Zeit, macht' ih - nen war - me Schuh'; und
mer - ry time; well shod from toe to heel; if

gu - te Zeit, macht' ih - nen war - me Schuh'; und
mer - ry time; well shod from toe to heel; if

wenn ihm Kei - ner 'sLe - der leiht, so stahl er sich's da-
lea - ther lacked, he thought no crime, and stole what he could

wenn ihm' Kei - ner 'sLe - der leiht, so stahl er sich's da-
lea - ther lacked, he thought no crime, and stole what he could

wenn ihm Kei - ner 'sLe - der leiht, so stahl er sich's da-
lea - ther lacked, he thought no crime, and stole what he could

wenn ihm Kei - ner 'sLe - der leiht, so stahl er sich's da-
lea - ther lacked, he thought no crime, and stole what he could

DIE SCHUSTER.
THE SHOEMAKERS.

zu. Der Schuster hat ein weit Ge - wis - sen macht
steal. A cob-bler's conscience is not queas - y, and

zu. Der Schuster hat ein weit Ge - wis - sen macht
steal. A cob-bler's conscience is not queas - y, and

zu. Der Schuster hat ein weit Ge - wis - sen macht
steal. A cob-bler's con-science is not queas - y, and

zu__ Der Schuster hat ein weit Ge - wis - sen macht
steal. A__ cob-bler's conscience is not queas - y, and

Schuhe selbst mit Hin - der - nis - - - - - sen; und ist vom
trifles make it not un - eas - - - - - y; when from the

Schuhe selbst mit Hin - der - nis - - - - sen; und ist vom
trifles make it not un - eas - - - - y; when from the

Schuhe selbst mit Hin - der - nis - - - - sen; und ist vom
trifles make it not un - eas - - - - y; when from the

Schuhe selbst mit Hin - der - nis - - - - sen; und ist vom
trifles make it not un - eas - - - - y; when from the

27327

472

DIE SCHUSTER.
THE SHOEMAKERS.

Ger - - - ber das Fell erst weg, dann streck', streck',
tan - - - ner the skin we get, *then beat, beat,*

Ger - - - ber das Fell erst weg, dann streck', streck',
tan - - - ner the skin we get, *then beat, beat,*

Ger - - ber das Fell erst weg, dann streck', streck',
tan - - - ner the skin we get, *then beat, beat,*

Ger - - ber das Fell erst weg, dann streck', streck',
tan - - - ner the skin we get, *then beat, beat,*

ƒ

P. P. P.

streck'! Le - der taugt nur am rech - ten Fleck.
beat! *Lea - ther serves but to shoe our feet.*

streck'! Le - der taugt nur am rech - ten Fleck.
beat! *Lea - ther serves but to shoe our feet.*

streck'! Le - der taugt nur am rech - ten Fleck.
beat! *Lea - ther serves but to shoe our feet.*

streck'! Le - der taugt nur am rech - ten Fleck.
beat! *Lea - ther serves but to shoe our feet.*

(Die Stadtwächter ziehen,
mit Trompeten und Trom-
meln, den Stadtpfeifern,
Lauthenmachern, u.s.w.
voraus.)
(The town watchmen, with
trumpets and drums come
on, followed by the town
pipers, lute makers etc.)

Trompeten auf dem Theater.
Trumpets on the stage.

Rührtrommeln. (a.d. Theater.)

ƒ

ƒ

P. P. P. P.

27327

(Gesellen mit Kinderinstrumenten.)
(*Journeymen with toy instruments.*)

Trompeten a.d.Theater. (*Trumpets on the stage.*)
Stadtwächter und Heerhornbläser.(*Town watchmen and Trumpeters.*)

Rührtrommeln (a.d.Theater.)

27327

*) Die Triller (tr) sind von den Sängern als sogenannte Bockstriller auszuführen.
The shakes (tr) are to be sung in imitation of a goat's bleating.

DIE SCHNEIDER.
THE TAILORS.

Stadt und Land ver-dor-ben gar, war nicht ein Schnei-der, ein Schneider, ein
done had been our town for good, were not a tai - lor, a tai - lor, a

Schnei-der zur Hand, der viel Muth hatt' und Ver - stand.
tai - lor at hand. Bold - ly then this trick he planned.

476

DIE SCHNEIDER.
THE TAILORS.

27327

DIE BÄCKER.
THE BAKERS.

gäb' euch der Bä-cker nicht täg-lich Brod, müsst' al - - le Welt ver -
bakers must bring us our dai-ly bread, or hun - - ger soon would

gäb' euch der Bä-cker nicht täg-lich Brod, müsst' al - - le Welt ver -
bakers must bring us our dai-ly bread, or hun - - ger soon would

gäb' euch der Bä-cker nicht täg-lich Brod, müsst' al - - le Welt ver -
bakers must bring us our dai-ly bread, or hun - - ger soon would

gäb' nicht der Bä-cker Brod, müsst' al - - le Welt ver -
bak - ers must bring us bread, or hun - - ger soon would

schei - - den. Beck! Beck! Beck! Täg-lich auf dem
end us. Wheat, wheat, wheat, makes the bread we

schei - - den. Beck! Beck! Beck! Täg-lich auf dem
end us. Wheat, wheat, wheat, makes the bread we

schei - - den. Beck! Beck! Beck! Täg-lich auf dem
end us. Wheat, wheat, wheat, makes the bread we

schei - - den. Beck! Beck! Beck! Täg-lich auf dem
end us. Wheat, wheat, wheat, makes the bread we

(Ein bunter Kahn mit jungen Mädchen in reicher bäuerischer Tracht kommt an. Die Lehrbuben laufen nach dem Gestade.)
(A decorated boat arrives full of young girls in rich peasants dresses. The Prentices run to the bank.)

(Das Charakteristische des folgenden Tanzes, mit welchem die Lehrbuben und Mädchen zunächst nach dem Vordergrund kommen, besteht darin, dass die Lehrbuben die Mädchen scheinbar nur am Platz bringen wollen; sowie die Gesellen zugreifen wollen, ziehen die Buben die Mädchen aber immer zurück, als ob sie sie anders wo unterbringen wollten, wobei sie meistens den ganzen Kreis, wie wählend, ausmessen, und somit die scheinbare Absicht auszuführen anmuthig und lustig verzögern.)

(The peculiarity of the following dance with which the Prentices and girls come to the front, is this: the Prentices apparently only wish to bring the girls to the open place, but, as the Journeymen keep trying to seize the girls, the Prentices draw them away as if seeking to take them to another place, whereby they make the tour of the whole stage, continually delaying their original purpose in good-natured fun.)

Mässiges Walzer-Zeitmass.

(David kommt vom Landungsplatze vor und sieht
(David comes forward from the landing place and

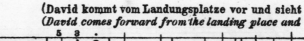

missbilligend dem Tanze zu.)
looks disapprovingly at the dancing.)

DAVID.

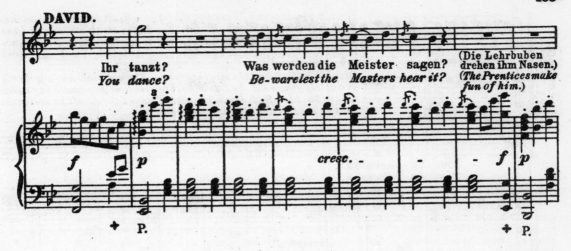

Ihr tanzt? Was werden die Meister sagen? (Die Lehrbuben
You dance? Be-warelest the Masters hear it? drehen ihm Nasen.)
(The Prentices make
fun of him.)

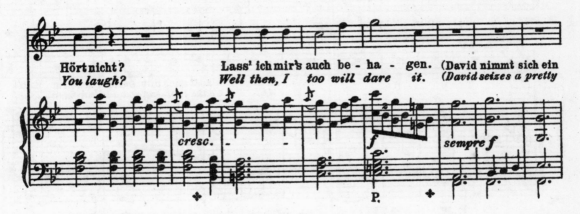

Hört nicht? Lass' ich mir's auch be - ha - gen. (David nimmt sich ein
You laugh? Well then, I too will dare it. (David seizes a pretty

junges schönes Mädchen, und geräth im Tanze mit ihr
schnell in grosses Feuer.)
young girl and joins in the dance with great ardour.)

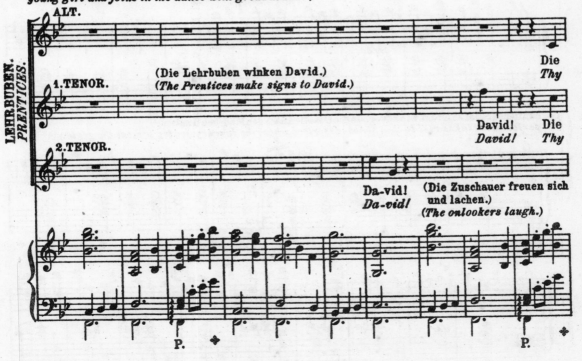

ALT.

Die
Thy

LEHRBUBEN.
PRENTICES.

1.TENOR.

(Die Lehrbuben winken David.)
(The Prentices make signs to David.)

David! Die
David! Thy

2.TENOR.

Da-vid! (Die Zuschauer freuen sich
Da-vid! und lachen.)
(The onlookers laugh.)

(Die Meistersinger ordnen sich am Landungsplatze zum festlichen Aufzuge.)
(*At the landing-place the Master-singers arrange themselves for a grand procession.*)

(Beginn des **Aufzuges**
der Meistersinger.)
(*The Master-singers'
procession starts.*)

(Hier kommt Kothner mit der Fahne im Vordergrunde an. Die geschwungene Fahne, auf welcher König Da-
(Here Kothner reaches the front with the banner bearing the portrait of king David with his harp, at sight of

vid mit der Harfe abgebildet ist, wird von allem Volk mit Hutschwenken begrüsst.)
which the people wave their hats.)

(Der Zug der Meistersinger ist hier auf der Singerbühne, wo Kothner die Fahne aufgepflanzt, angelangt:
Pogner, Eva an der Hand führend, diese von festlich geschmückten und reichgekleideten Mädchen, unter
denen auch Magdalene, begleitet, voran.)
(*The procession of the Master-singers has now reached the platform, where Kothner plants the banner: Pogner
leading forward Eva by the hand. She is accompanied by girls richly dressed; among them is Magdalene.*)

(Trompeten auf dem Theater.)
(*Trumpets on the stage.*)

(Als Eva, von den Mädchen umgeben, den mit Blumen geschmückten Ehrenplatz eingenommen, und alle
Übrigen, die Meister auf den Bänken, die Gesellen hinter ihnen stehend, ebenfalls Platz genommen,
treten die Lehrbuben, dem Volke zugewendet, feierlich vor der Bühne in Reih' und Glied.)
(When Eva, surrounded by the girls, has taken the flower strewn place of honour and all the rest are
in their places, the Masters on the benches, the Journeymen standing behind them, the Prentices ad-
vance to the platform in proper order and turn round to the people.)

LEHRBUBEN. PRENTICES.

ALT.
Si - lenti - um!
Si - lenti - um!
Si - lenti - um!
Si - lenti - um!

1.TEN.
Si - lenti - um!
Si - lenti - um!
Si - lenti - um!
Si - lenti - um!

2.TEN.
Si - lenti - um!
Si - lenti - um!
Si - lenti - um!
Si - lenti - um!

1.ALT.
Macht kein Re - den und kein Ge -
Speak no word,_____ let no sound be

2.ALT.
Macht kein Re - den und kein Ge -
Speak no word, let no sound be

1.TEN.
Macht kein Re - den und kein Ge -
Speak no word, let no sound be

2.TEN.
Macht kein Re - den und kein Ge -
Speak no word, let no sound be

VOLK.
(Sachs erhebt sich und tritt vor.
Bei seinem Anblick stösst sich Alles an;
Hüte und Mützen werden abgezogen: Alle deuten auf ihn.)
(Sachs rises and comes forward. At the sight of him, all
press forward, hats and caps are doffed. All point to him.)

494

27327

496

27327

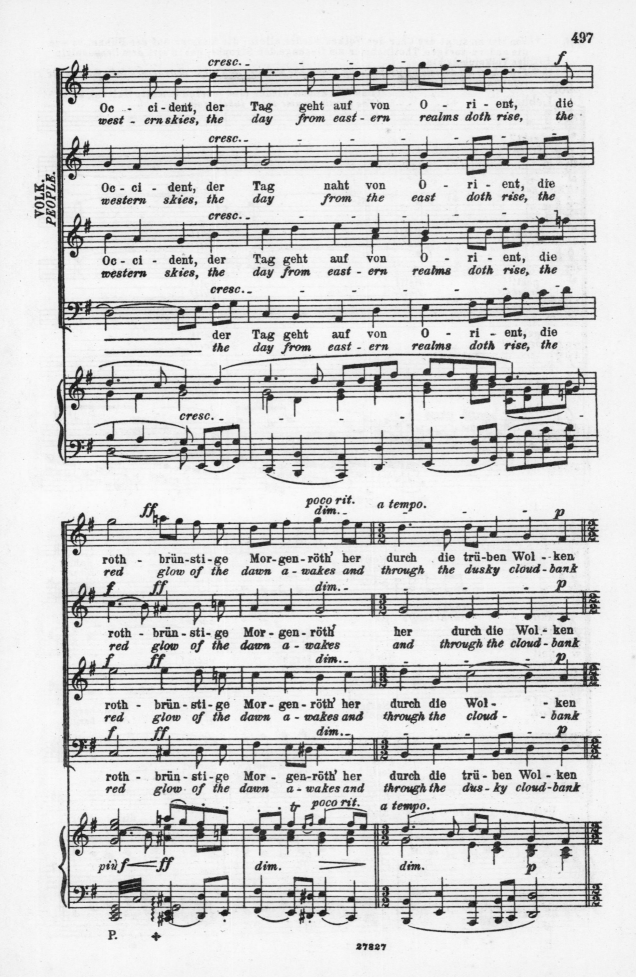

498

+) Von hier an singt der Chor des Volkes wieder allein; die Meister auf der Bühne, so wie die andern vorigen Theilnehmer am Gesange der Strophe, geben sich dem Schauspiele des Volksjubels hin.
+) From here the chorus of people sing alone: the Masters and other characters take part in the rejoicings of the people.

Sehr mässig und zögernd.

SACHS (der unbeweglich, wie geistesabwesend, über die Volksmenge hinweg geblickt hatte, richtet endlich seine Blicke vertrauter auf sie, und beginnt mit ergriffener, schnell aber sich festigender Stimme.)
(who motionless, as if wrapt in thought, has been gazing far away over the crowd, at length turns his eyes with kindly expression on them and begins in a voice at first veiled by emotion but quickly becoming firmer.)

Euch macht ihr's leicht, mir macht ihr's schwer, gebt ihr mir Armen zu viel Ehr'.
Words light to you bow me to earth: your praise is far beyond my worth.

SACHS.

Soll vor der Ehr' ich be-steh'n, sei's mich von euch ge - liebt _____ zu
One on-ly hon- our be mine, 'tis this, that I your love _____ may

sehn.
win.

Schon gros-se Ehr' _____ ward mir er-
The high-est hon - - our you pro-

kannt, ward heut' ich zum Spruch-spre-cher er-nannt.
claimed for me, when as spokes-man I was named:

Und was mein Spruch euch kün-den
and all my speech, now heed it

soll, glaubt, das ist ho - her Eh - ren voll. Wenn ihr die Kunst so hoch schon
well! sooth, shall a tale of hon - our tell. If art so high is prized by

SACHS.

ehrt,   da galt es zu be-wei-sen, dass,wer ihr selbst gar an-ge-
you,   I fain would show you clearly, that one who lives her servant

hört,   sie schätzt ob al-len Prei-sen. Ein Meister,reich und hoch-ge-
true   o'er all doth love her dear-ly. A Master rich and high in

muth,   der will heut' euch das zei-gen: sein Töch- - -ter
worth,   his love now lets you mea-sure: his daugh- -ter

lein,___ sein höch- -stes Gut, mit al-lemHab' und
fair,___ his best_____ on earth, with all his gold and

504

SACHS.

traut,___ euch ruf' ich's vor dem Vol - - ke laut:
day,__ to you be-fore all folk I say:

erwägt der Wer - bung selt'nen Preis, und wem__ sie soll ge -
think well how rare__ a prize is here, that each__ may surely

lin - gen, dass der sich rein und e - del weiss im
bring her a heart and voice both pure and clear, as

BECKM. (zu dem sich jetzt Sachs wendet, hat schon während des Einzuges, und dann fortwährend eifrig das Blatt mit dem Gedicht herausgezogen, memorirt, genau zu lesen versucht, und oft
verzweiflungsvoll sich den Schweiss getrocknet.)
(to whom Sachs now turns, has all through been constantly taking the poem from his
pocket and trying to learn it by heart, often wiping the sweat from his brow in
despair.)

KOTHN.

Macht euch be-reit! Der Ael - test'sich zu - erstan - lässt! Herr
be ye prepared! *The old - est man shall first be heard.* *Friend*

Beckmesser, ihr fangt an:____ 'sist Zeit!
Beckmesser, you be - gin:____ 'tis time!

(Die Lehrbuben führen Beckmesser zu einem kleinen Rasenhügel vor der
Singerbühne, welchen sie zuvor festgerammelt, und reich mit Blumen über-
deckt haben; Beckmesser strauchelt darauf, tritt unsicher und schwankt.)
*(The Prentices lead Beckmesser to a small mound of turf in front of the
platform which they have previously made and firmly rammed down and decorated with flowers, Beckmesser stumbles on to it, and stands tottering and insecure-
ly.)* **Leicht und lebhaft.**

BECKM.

ZumTeufel! Wiewackelig!
The devil! How rickety!

BECKM.

Macht das hübsch fest!
Just make that firm!

(Die Buben lachen unter sich und stopfen lustig an dem Rasen.)
(The prentices laugh among themselves and ram down the turf.)

poco a poco cresc.

(Das Volk stösst sich gegenseitig lustig an.)
(The people humourously nudge one another.)

1. ALT.

Der
He

2. ALT.

Der?
He?

3. ALT.

Wie?
What?

1. TEN.

Der wirbt?
He woos?

2. TEN.

Der?
He?

3. TEN.

Wie?
What?

VOLK.
PEOPLE.

1. BASS.

Scheint mir nicht der Rechte!
Sure-ly she'll refuse him!

2. BASS.

Scheint mir nicht der Rechte!
Sure-ly she'll refuse him!

f   dim.   p

27327

(Beckmesser, der sich endlich mit Mühe auf dem Rasenhügel festgestellt hat, macht eine erste Verbeugung gegen die Meister, eine zweite gegen das Volk, dann gegen Eva, auf welche er, da sie sich abwendet, nochmals verle-

(Beckmesser, who with trouble has at length found firm footing on the mound, bows first to the Masters, then to the people and then to Eva, at whom, when she turns away, he again blinks with embarrassment; he

gen hinblinzelt; grosse Beklommenheit erfasst ihn; er sucht sich durch ein Vorspiel auf der Laute zu ermuthigen.)

tries to calm his uneasiness by a prelude on the lute.)

BECKM.

LAUTE.

„Mor-gen ich leuchte in
"Bathing in sunlight at
(„Mor - gen - lich leuch-tend in
("Bathed in the sun-light at

ro - sigem Schein, von Blut und Duft geht schnell die Luft; wohl bald ge-won - - nen, wie zer-
dawning of day, with bo-som bare, to greet the air; my beauty steam - ing, fast er

ro - si-gem Schein, von Blüth und Duft ge-schwellt die Luft, voll al-ler Won - - nen, nie er-
dawn of the day, when blos-soms rare made sweet the air, with beauties teem - ing, past all

ron - - nen; im Gar-ten lud_____ ich ein garstig und fein."
dream - ing; a gar-den round - - - e-lay wearied my way."

son - - nen, ein Gar-ten lud_____ mich ein; Gast ihm zu sein.")
dream - - ing, a gar-den round_____ me lay, cheer - ing my way.")

(Beckmesser richtet sich wieder ein, besser auf den Füssen zu stehen.)
(Beckmesser again attempts to gain a better footing.)
(Die Meistersinger leise unter sich.)
(The Mastersingers softly to each other.)

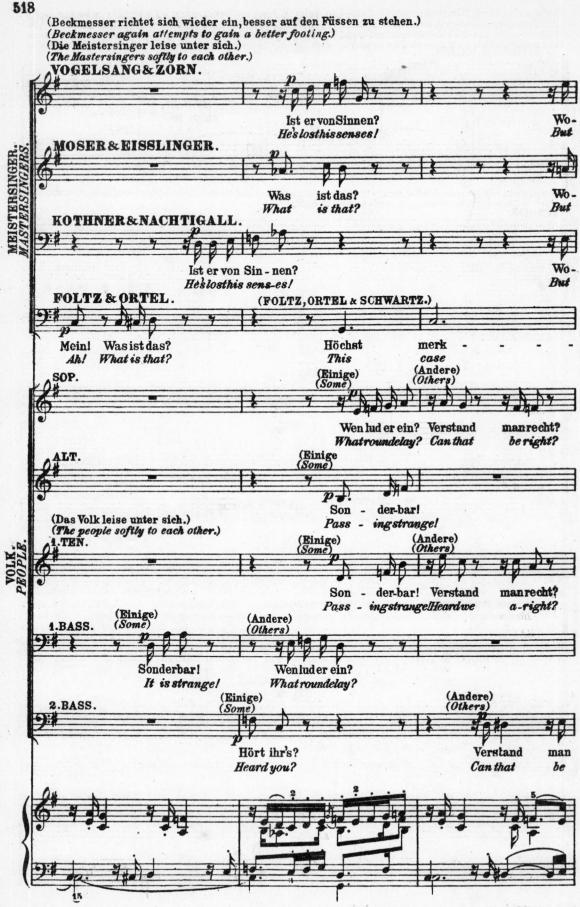

15

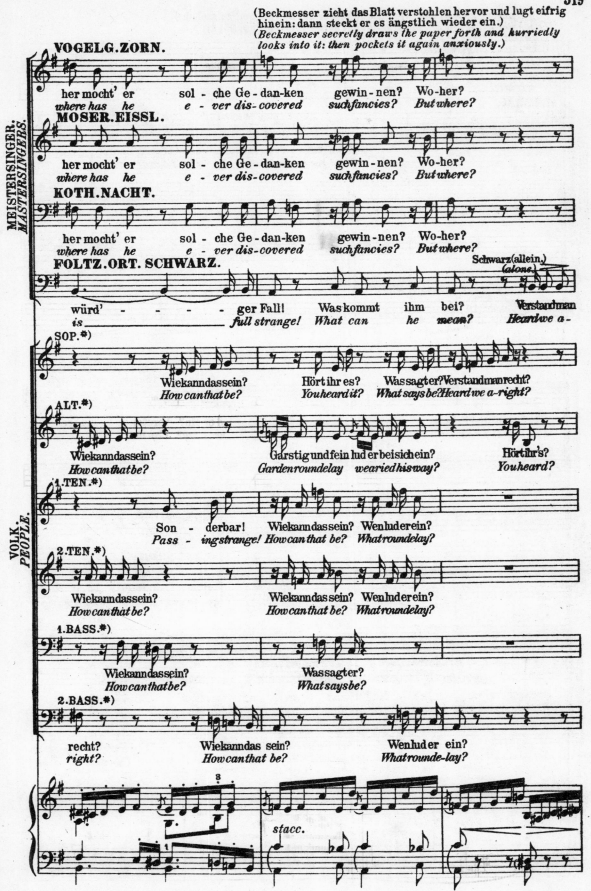

BECKM.

Verdammter Schu - ster, das dank' ich dir! Das
Ac-cursed cob - bler, yours the de - sign! *The*

Lied, es ist gar nicht von mir: vom Sachs der
song, in sooth, is none of mine: 'twas Sachs whom

hier so hoch ver - ehrt, von eu - rem Sachs ward mir's be - scheert. Mich hat der
ye so much re - vere, that wrote the song I sang you here! Now through his

Schänd - li - che be - drängt, sein schlechtes Lied mir auf - ge - hängt.
shame - ful trick I see! His worth - less stuff he puts on me.

(Er stürzt wüthend
(*He rushes away*

27327

SACHS.

Von hier an merk-

Beck - mes - ser irrt, wie dort so hier.
Beck - mes - ser errs, both here and there.

Sehr ruhig.

più p

p dolce scherz.

lich langsamer geworden.

Wie er da - zu kam, mag selbster sagen; doch möcht'
Let him now to all tell where he got it; for my-

ich nie mich zu rüh - - men wa - gen, ein Lied, so
self, I dare not boast___ I wrote it; nor yet that

poco cresc.

p

schön wie dies er - dacht, sei von mir Hans Sachs ge -
aught so no - bly fine as this song could e'er be -

dim.

dim.

più p

27327

Wei - se hier Ei - ner säng' im Krei - se; und wer dies ver-
mong you, the words be right-ly sung you; and he who that

stünd' zu-gleich be - wies', dass er des Lie - des Dich - ter und
truth can bring to light, will prove him - self the po - et and

gar mit Rech - te Mei - ster hiess', fänd' er ge-rech - te Rich - ter.
Mas - ter - sing - er, too, by right: all who have ears will know it.

Ich bin ver - klagt, und muss be - steh'n: drum lasst mich mei - nen
I am ac - cused, and take my stand: my wit - ness let me

poco rallent.

SACHS.

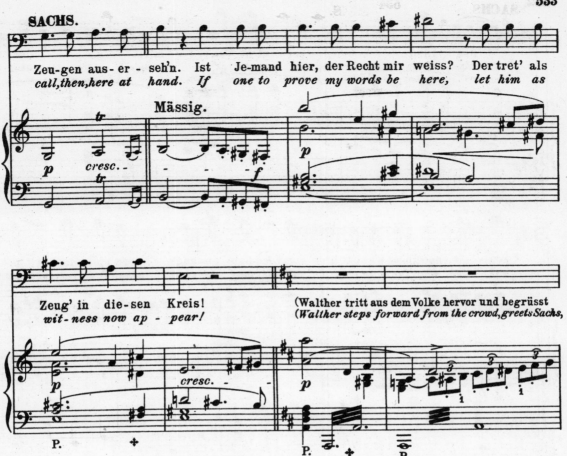

Zeu-gen aus- er - seh'n. Ist Je-mand hier, der Recht mir weiss? Der tret' als
call, then, here at hand. If one to prove my words be here, let him as

Mässig.

Zeug' in die-sen Kreis!
wit - ness now ap - pear!

(Walther tritt aus dem Volke hervor und begrüsst
(*Walther steps forward from the crowd, greets Sachs,*

Sachs, sodann nach den beiden Seiten hin die Meister und das Volk mit ritterlicher Freundlichkeit. Es entsteht sogleich eine angenehme Bewegung. Alles weilt einen Augenblick schweigend in seiner Betrachtung.)
and then the Masters and the people in turn, with knightly courtesy. A movement of pleasure takes place.
All remain silent for a short time, observing him.)

SACHS.

So zeu - get,
Bear wit - ness,

(Walther beschreitet festen Schrittes den kleinen Blumenhügel.)
(Walther firmly steps on to the mound.)

Sehr mässig.

(sehr lang)
(molto ten.)

WALTH.

„Mor - gen-lich leuch-tend im
"Bathed in the sun-light at

ro - si - gen Schein, von Blüth' und Duft ge-schwellt die Luft, voll al - ler
dawn - ing of day, while blossoms rare made sweet the air, with beauties

(anschwellend.)
(cresc.)

(An dieser Stelle lässt Kothner das Blatt, in welchem er mit den andern Meistern eifrig nachzulesen begonnen, vor Ergriffenheit unwillkürlich fallen, er und die Uebrigen hören nur noch theilnamvoll zu.)
(*Kothner, who with the other Masters had begun to follow the written words of the song, deeply moved, here lets the paper fall. He and the rest listen with interest.*)

WALTH.

Won — — nen nie er-son-nen, ein Garten lud mich ein, dort un-ter ei-nem
teem — — ing past all dreaming, a garden round me lay, and there beneath a

Wun-der-baum, von Früch-ten reich be - han-gen, zu schau'n in sel' - gem
wondrous tree, where fruits were rich-ly throng-ing, my bliss - ful dream re -

Lie - bestraum, was höchstem Lust - ver - lan-gen Er - ful-lung kühn ver -
vealed to me the goal of all my long-ing, and life's most glor - ious

hiess, das schön - ste Weib: _____ E - va im Pa - ra-
prize, a wo - man fair: _____ E - va in Pa - ra-

541

27327

A - bend-lich düm-mernd um - schloss mich die Nacht; auf stei-lem Pfad war ich ge-
Dark-ness had fall-en____ and night closed me round; on ston-y road my foot-steps

naht zu ei - ner Quel - le rei - ner Wel - le, die
trod, where on a mount-ain rose a fount-ain that

lo - ckend mir _____ ge - lacht: dort un - ter ei - nem
lured my feet _____ with its sound: there un - der-neath a

Lor - beer - baum, von Ster - nen hell durch -
lau - rel tree, where stars like fruit were

WALTH.

Tag, dem ich aus Dichter's Traum er - wacht! Das ich er - träumt, das Pa - ra -
day, on which my po-et's dream took flight! That Pa - ra - dise my vision

dies, in himmlisch neu verklärter Pracht, hell vor mir
shewed, revealed a - new in Heaven's light, shin - ing now

lag, da - hin lachend nun der Quell den Pfad mir wies; die
lay; there-to point - ing the path, a laughing streamlet flowed, and

dort ge - bo - ren, mein Herz er - ko - ren, der
gleam - ing yón - der, a ra - diant won - der, the

27327

WALTH.

Er - de lieb - lich - stes Bild, als Mu - se mir ge - weiht, so hei -
garden's maid - en so fair, as Muse be - fore me stood in ho -

- lig ernst als mild, ward kühn von mir ge -
- ly calm - ness there. That maid I bold - ly

freit; am lich - ten Tag der Son - nen, durch San - ges Sieg ge -
wooed; and there in light of Hea - ven, the prize of song was

SOP.

Ge - wiegt wie in den
En - chant - - - ed by this

ALT.

Ge - wiegt wie in den schön - sten
En - chant - ed by this beau - teous

TEN.

Ge - wiegt wie in den schön - sten
En - chant - ed by this beau - teous

BASS.

Ge - wiegt in Traum,
En - chant - ing strain,

VOLK.
PEOPLE.

550

POGNER (mit grosser Ergriffenheit zu Sachs sich wendend.)
(turning to Sachs with deep emotion.)

27327

POGNER.

Sachs! ———— Dir dank' ich Glück und Ehr': vor-
Sachs! ———— Thou bring'st me peace at last: now

MEISTERSINGER.
MASTERSINGERS.

Mei - ster - preis, den Mei - ster - preis! Reich' das
Mas - ter's crown, the Mas - ter's crown! Grant his

Mei - ster - preis, den Mei - ster - preis! Kei - ner
Mas - ter's crown, the Mas - ter's crown! Right so

Mei - ster - preis, den Mei - ster - preis! Kei - ner
Mas - ter's crown, the Mas - ter's crown! Right so

Mei - ster - preis, den Mei - ster - preis! Kei - ner
Mas - ter's crown, the Mas - ter's crown! Right so

SOP.

Preis, sein der Preis; Kei - ner wie er zu wer - ben weiss; reich' ihm das
crown, his the crown. Right such as his none here hath shown; grant him his

ALT.

er zu wer - ben weiss, Kei - ner wie er zu wer - ben weiss; reich'
his none here hath shown; right such as his none here hath shown; grant

1.TEN.

er zu wer - ben weiss; reich' das Reis, sein der Preis! Reich' das
his none here hath shown. Grant his own; his the crown! Grant his

2.TEN.

Preis, sein der Preis, das Reis und der Preis! Kei - ner
crown, his the crown; his own; his the crown! Right so

1.BASS.

Reis, sein das Reis und der Preis! Kei - ner
own, his the crown, his the crown! Right so

2.BASS.

Reis, ihm das Reis, sein der Preis, sein der Preis! Kei - ner
own, 'tis his own, his the crown, his the crown! Right so

VOLK.
PEOPLE.

cresc. poco f p

P. ⊕ P. ⊕

27327

(Walther ist auf die
Stufen der Singerbüh-
(Walther has been con-

POGNER.

ü - ber nun all' Herz - be - schwer!
all my heart's dis - tress is past!

MEISTERSINGER.
MASTERSINGERS.

Reis, sein der Preis: Kei - - - ner, Kei - ner
own; his the crown: right so clear as

so, wie nur er zu wer - ben weiss, wie
clear to the crown none here hath shown, such

so, wie nur er, wie er zu wer - ben
clear none hath shown, a right so clear as

so, wie nur er zu wer - ben weiss
clear none hath shown but he a - lone

SOPR.
Reis, sein der Preis, sein der Preis! Kei - ner wie
own; his the crown, his the crown! No - one but

ALT.
ihm, reich' ihm den Preis! Denn Kei - ner
him, grant him the crown! A right so

1.TEN.
Reis, sein der Preis, Kei - - - ner, Kei - ner
own; his the crown! Right so clear as

2.TEN.
so, wie nur er zu wer - ben weiss, wie
clear to the crown none here hath shown. Such

VOLK.
PEOPLE.

1.BASS.
so, wie nur er, wie er zu wer - ben
clear none hath shown, such right none here hath

2.BASS.
so, wie nur er zu wer - ben weiss
clear to the crown none here hath shown

cresc.

f

P.

ne geleitet worden und lässt sich dort vor Eva auf ein Knie nieder.)
ducted to the steps of the platform and there kneels on one knee before Eva.)

(Eva zu Walther, indem sie ihn mit einem Kranz aus Lorbeer und Myrthen bekränzt, sich hinabneigend.)
(Eva to Walther, as she stoops down and crowns him with a wreath of laurels and myrtles.)

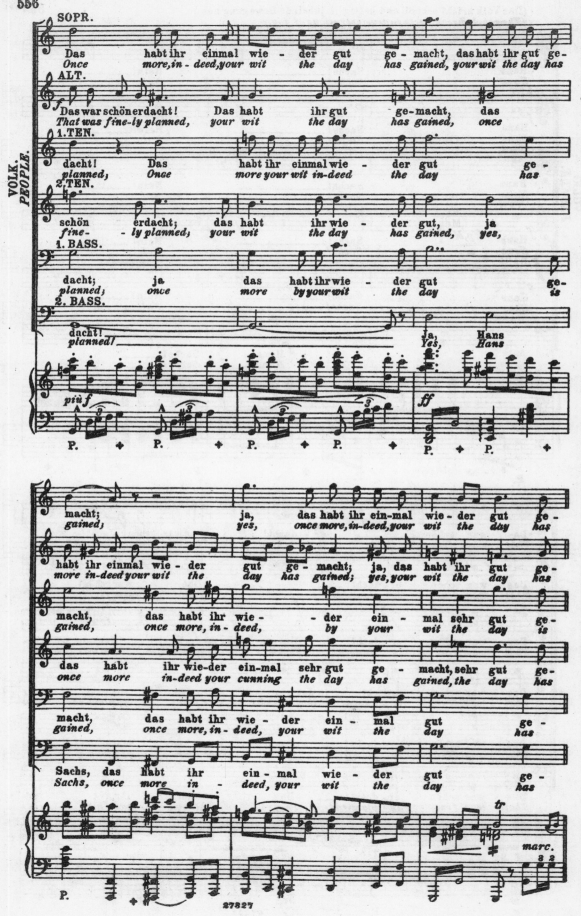

SOPR.

Das habt ihr einmal wie - der gut ge - macht, das habt ihr gut ge-
Once more, in - deed, your wit the day has gained, your wit the day has

ALT.

Das war schön er dacht! Das habt ihr gut ge-macht, das
That was fine-ly planned, your wit the day has gained, once

VOLK.
PEOPLE.

1.TEN.

dacht! Das habt ihr einmal wie - der gut ge-
planned; Once more your wit in-deed the day has

2.TEN.

schön er dacht; das habt ihr wie - der gut, ja
fine- ly planned; your wit the day has gained, yes,

1.BASS.

dacht; ja das habt ihr wie - der gut ge-
planned; once more by your wit the day is

2.BASS.

dacht! ja, Hans
planned! Yes, Hans

più f
ff

P.   P.   P.   P.   P.   P.

macht; ja, das habt ihr ein-mal wie - der gut ge-
gained; yes, once more, in-deed, your wit the day has

habt ihr einmal wie - der gut ge - macht; ja, das habt ihr gut ge-
more in-deed your wit the day has gained; yes, your wit the day has

macht, das habt ihr wie - der ein - mal sehr gut ge-
gained, once more, in - deed, by your wit the day is

das habt ihr wie-der ein-mal sehr gut ge - macht, sehr gut ge-
once more in-deed your cunning the day has gained, the day has

macht, das habt ihr wie - der ein - mal gut ge-
gained, once more, in - deed, your wit the day has

Sachs, das habt ihr ein - mal wie - der gut ge-
Sachs, once more in - deed, your wit the day has

marc.
3 2

P.

27327

POGNER.

schmückt mit Kö - nig Da - vid's Bild,
Da - vid's like-ness take from me,

nehm'
of the

Mässig.

dolce

ich euch auf in der Meis-ter Gild'!
Masters' Guild thus I make you free!

dolce

WALTH.(mit schmerzlicher Heftigkeit abweisend.)
(refusing the chain impetuonsly.)

(Er blickt zärtlich auf Eva.)
(He looks tenderly at Eva.)

Nicht Meister! Nein!
Not Master! No!

Will oh - ne Meister se - lig
One better way to Heav'n I

Langsam.

dim.

dolce

(Alles blickt mit grosser Betroffenheit auf Sachs.)
(All look at Sachs in great perplexity.)

sein!
know!

cresc.

dim.

27327

(Sachs schreitet auf Walther zu, und fasst ihn bedeutungsvoll bei der Hand.)
(Sachs comes to Walther and takes him impressively by the hand.)

SACHS.

Mässig bewegt.

Ver-ach-tet mir die Meis-ter nicht, und
Dis-dain our Mas-ters not, my friend, and

ehrt mir ih - re Kunst! Was ih-nen hoch zum Lo - be
hon-our well their art! What, to their glo-ry, art has

immer mässig gestossen.

spricht, fiel reichlich euch zur Gunst. Nicht eu-ren Ah - nen noch___ so
gained, right well has ta'en your part. For not your an-ces-tors___ or

werth, nicht eurem Wappen, Speer noch Schwert,— dass ihr ein Dich - ter seid, ein
birth, nor crest and banner, sword of worth; your po-et's song a-lone the

Meis - ter euch ge-freit; — dem — dankt ihr heut' eu'r höch - stes
Mas - ter's crown hath won; — *that — brings to-day your high - est*

cresc. -

P. ✦

Glück. Drum denkt mit Dank — ihr dran zu - rück, wie kann die Kunst wohl
bliss. Then think with thank - - ful-ness on this. How can that art be

f dim. p ausdrucksvoll.

P. ✦ P ✦ *gehalten.* P. ✦

un - werth sein, die sol - - che Prei - se schliesset
held as naught, that prize so rare as this has

cresc. - mf p cresc. -

P. ✦ P. ✦ P. ✦

ein? Dass uns're Meister sie ge-pflegt grad' recht nach ih - rer
brought? Right well our Masters' Guild did tend our art, and ne - ver

f ³ p

SACHS.

Art, nach ih-rem Sin-ne treu ge-hegt, das hat sie echt be - wahrt:bliebsienicht
swerved from truth and right to gain their end; thus was our art pre-served: and though not

stacc. poco cresc. - - - poco f p

ad'- lig, wie zur Zeit, wo Höf' und Fürsten sie ge - weiht; im Drang der schlimmen
hon-oured as of old, when courts and kings her glories told; when strife and tur- moil

p poco cresc. -

Jahr' blieb sie doch deutsch und wahr: und wär' sie an-ders nicht ge -
grew, German she stood and true: and though she veiled her worth-i -

f p

glückt, als wie wo Al - les drängt und drückt, ihr seht wie hoch sie blieb in Ehr': was
ness, a-mid the mighty storm and stress, you see, her fame is high and sure: what

cresc. - tr

SACHS.

wollt ihr von den Meistern mehr?
would you from the Mas-ters more?
Habt Acht!
Be - ware!
Uns
Ill

dräu - en üb - le Streich';
times now threaten all;
zerfällt erst deutsches Volk und Reich, in
if we Germans should e - ver fall in

falscher wälscher Majestät kein Fürst bald mehr sein Volk versteht, und wälschen Dunst mit wälschem
thrall to a - ny foreign land, no prince his folk will un-der-stand, and foreign mists will blind our

Tand sie pflanzen uns in deutsches Land; was deutsch und echt, wüsst' Kei-ner mehr, lebt's nicht in
eyes, and o'er our German land will rise: the art we own were lost for aye, liv-ing in

SACHS.

deut - scher Meis - ter Ehr'.   Drum   sag' ich euch:
Ger - man song to - day.   Then   hear me now:

Etwas zurückhaltend.   *In das frühere Zeitmass zurückkehrend.*

ehrt   eu - re deut - - schen Meis - ter!   Dann
hon - - our your Ger - - man Mas - ters,   if

bannt ihr gu - - te Geis - ter;   und gebt ____ ihr   ihrem
you would shun dis - as - ters;   let each ____ hold   them

Während des folgenden Schlussgesanges nimmt Eva den Kranz von Walthers Stirne und drückt ihn Sachs auf; dieser nimmt die Kette aus Pogner's Hand, und hängt sie Walther um.
Nachdem Sachs das Paar umarmt, bleiben Walther und Eva zu beiden Seiten an Sachsen's Schultern gestützt; Pogner lässt sich, wie huldigend, auf ein Knie vor Sachs nieder. Die Meistersinger deuten mit erhobenen Händen auf Sachs, als auf ihr Haupt. Alle Anwesenden schliessen sich dem Gesange des Volkes an.
During the following finale Eva takes the wreath from Walther's head and places it on Sachs, who takes the chain from Pogner's hand, and hangs it round Walther's neck.
After Sachs has embraced the pair, Walther and Eva remain one on each side of him leaning on his shoulders. Pogner kneels as if in homage before Sachs. The Mastersingers point to Sachs with upraised hands as to their chief. All present join in the song of the people.

+) Von Allen mitzusingen, schliesslich auch von Walther und Eva.
To be sung by all, finally also by Walther and Eva.

27827

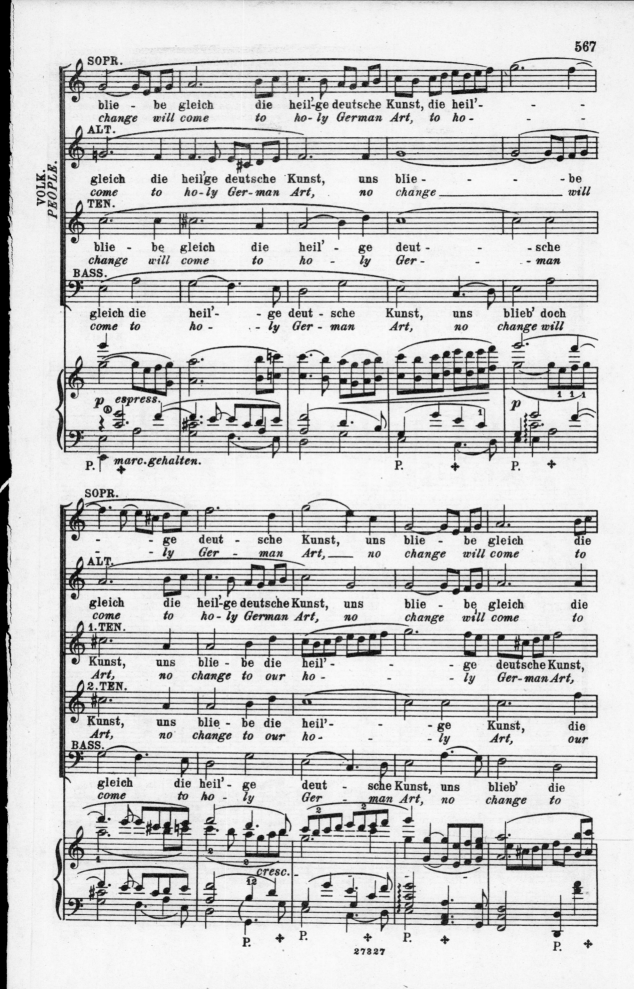

568

(Als es hier zu der bezeichneten Schlussgruppe
gelangt ist, schwenkt das Volk begeistert Hüte
und Tücher; die Lehrbuben tanzen und schlagen
jauchzend in die Hände.)
*(The final tableau is here reached. The people
wave hats and kerchiefs in excitement, the
Prentices dance and joyously clap their
hands.)*

27827